ESSENTIAL COPING SKILLS

WORKBOOK FOR TEENS

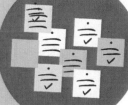

Master CBT & DBT Techniques to Unlock Your Emotional Superpowers, Conquer Life's Challenges, and Boost Personal Growth

ISABELLA FINN

Your 3 Complimentary E-books!

It's easy, just scan the QR code with the camera on your phone below to get full access or go to https://www.isabellafinn.com/coping-skills-bonuses

As an EXTRA Bonus - You get the Essential Coping Workbook for Teens in full color. Just scan with your phone below:

Join our parent support group on facebook

Feel free to email me at isabella@isabellafinn.com

Table of Contents

ESSENTIAL COPING SKILLS WORKBOOK FOR TEENS

Introduction

Have you ever had to do a class presentation, and the thought of it makes your heart pound, your palms sweat, and your stomach churn? Or maybe you've stood in front of a mirror, analyzing every flaw on your body, wishing you looked different. Or perhaps you've felt distressed because you failed your math test or you didn't make the sports team. Do any of these scenarios sound familiar?

The truth is, we've all been there. We've had days when it felt like our emotions were on a rollercoaster without seatbelts, leaving us confused and dizzy. We've been weighed down by stress as we juggled school, chores, social media, and friendships. During those times, it felt like we were speaking a different language than everyone else, and like we were carrying a backpack of worries around everywhere we went. We had moments when we looked in the mirror and wondered if we'll ever be enough in a world that's constantly changing its standards and demanding so much from teens.

Being a teenager isn't always what it looks like in the movies. It isn't all parties and perfect Instagram pictures. Sometimes it can be a wild roller coaster ride filled with intense emotions and it can feel like you're hanging on a thread.

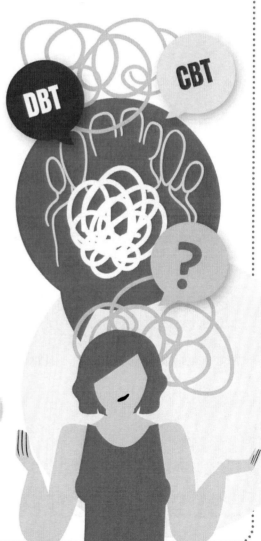

But regardless of your experience, never forget that **you're stronger than you think.** You have the power to pause, take a breather, and be in control of your experiences.

The human brain is wired to go bonkers when something is scary or we don't understand it. You know how it feels to try and solve a puzzle without all the pieces? That's how you'll feel — all over the place, with your emotions spiraling out of control.

But what if I told you that **you can unlock the superpower within you with two amazing therapies** in your toolkit to deal with the challenges you face daily?

Cognitive behavioral therapy (CBT) and **dialectical behavior therapy (DBT)** have proven effective in helping teenagers navigate the adventure of their teenage years. Learning the techniques is like having a stash of superpowers to help you survive and own your adolescence. In this book, CBT and DBT will serve as your guides and trusted allies in this endeavor.

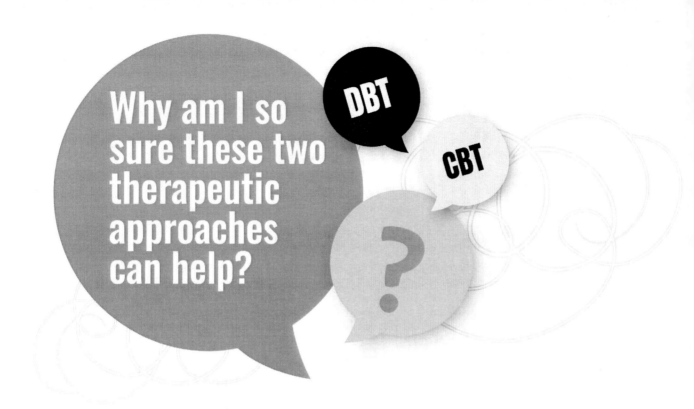

Why am I so sure these two therapeutic approaches can help?

DBT

CBT

?

Because I've been exactly where you are: I dealt with painful emotions, navigated the stormy seas of adolescence, stood on the front lines of teenage drama, and had my fair share of emotional breakdowns along the way. I've had sleepless nights, staring at the ceiling and wondering what in the world is going on. This continued for many years before I was introduced to CBT and DBT — the two therapies that saved my life. Using the skills and techniques has been an awesome journey, and I can't wait to spill the beans.

Besides being an author deeply connected to teenage mental health, I am a mom of two who helped her teens navigate those intense moments and guided them toward meaningful and fulfilling lives.

Every teenager out there is battling their own set of challenges.
In the following pages, you'll not only find answers to many of the questions bugging you, but also a sense of belonging.

Whether you hope to decode the intense emotions you feel, kick anxiety to the curb, engage in personal growth, or live a healthier life, this book is here to help you unlock your **emotional superpowers** and conquer the daily challenges of being a teenager.

Ready to dive into this adventure?
Let's get started!

Chapter 1
Understanding CBT and DBT

> "You have the power to change your thoughts, and your thoughts have the power to change your life."
>
> —Ron Willingham

What comes to your mind when you hear the word "therapy"?

As a teen, I always got scared! I wasn't open to therapy due to what I've seen in movies, where a shrink sits across from you with a notebook in their hands, ready to drill you with personal questions. That was scary for me; I wasn't ready to divulge my secrets to a stranger.

I felt this way because I didn't understand the idea of therapy back then. Thankfully, I learned and was eventually wowed by all the things I gained from certain types of therapy.

In the field of psychology, there are many types of therapy. However, **cognitive behavioral therapy (CBT)** and **dialectical behavior therapy (DBT)** are famous for helping teens navigate the ups and downs of adolescence. With the skills and techniques of these therapy methods, you can manage your emotions, build superhero-level confidence, conquer stress like a boss, and soar through your teenage years.

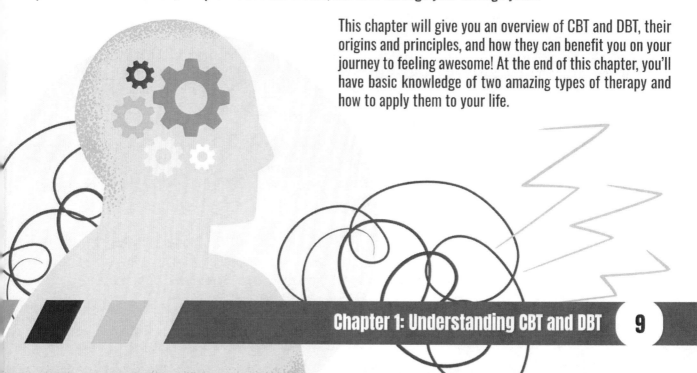

This chapter will give you an overview of CBT and DBT, their origins and principles, and how they can benefit you on your journey to feeling awesome! At the end of this chapter, you'll have basic knowledge of two amazing types of therapy and how to apply them to your life.

Cognitive behavioral therapy, or CBT for short, is a widely practiced form of psychotherapy that helps individuals address behavioral and emotional challenges. It's like having a personal life coach to help you calm your mind and master your emotions.

The American Psychological Association (APA) defines CBT as "a form of psychotherapy that integrates theories of cognition and learning with treatment techniques derived from cognitive therapy and behavior therapy. CBT assumes that cognitive, emotional, and behavioral variables are functionally interrelated."

So, how did CBT come about?

> In the 1960s, psychiatrist Aaron Beck and psychotherapist Albert Ellis realized that the traditional type of therapy we are all familiar with — the one we see in movies where the therapist holds a notepad, wears glasses, and asks questions — could be upgraded to something more goal-oriented and effective.
>
> They believed people could benefit from something more practical to help them deal with their day-to-day struggles. They combined two big ideas — cognitive therapy and behavioral therapy — to form CBT. Cognitive therapy focuses on thoughts, and behavioral therapy is about what you do in response to thoughts and feelings. CBT suggests that your thoughts, feelings, and actions are connected. If you can change your thoughts, you can change your feelings and reactions.

Now, let's talk about the **core principles** of this therapeutic approach:

Thoughts Take the Lead: In CBT, your thoughts steer the course while your feelings and actions follow its lead. It's believed that if you can change your thoughts, you can change your feelings and behaviors. Imagine you're in school, having a rough day, and then you start thinking, I am wasting my time here; I will never be good at this. This thought is powerful enough to steer your emotions, making you sad and frustrated.

The ABCs of CBT: CBT follows a formula called the ABC model. The A stands for "activating event," and is the thing that happens. B is "belief," your thoughts. And C is "consequence," how you feel and react afterward. CBT helps demonstrate how your B influences your C. It's like a domino effect — when your thought tips over, there will be a chain reaction of emotions and behaviors.

Mind Over Mood: I bet you've heard the saying, "Mind over matter." CBT proves that there's truth to this by showing that you can take charge of your thoughts and, as a result, your emotions and actions. CBT gives you a remote to control your brain and teaches you how to use it through its techniques.

From Baby Steps to Big Changes: Rome wasn't built in a day. According to CBT, you can't form new habits or ways of thinking immediately — you need to take small, consistent, manageable steps toward the change you want.

The Now Is What Matters: CBT encourages us to focus on what's happening right now rather than worry about the past and what is to come.

Remember, CBT doesn't encourage you to ignore your problems and pretend that all is well. Rather, it encourages you to face your issues head-on by understanding your thoughts and learning practical strategies for riding out the storm.

The Children's and Adult Center for OCD and Anxiety states that 70–80% of teens who engage in CBT respond to it well, and it provides lasting results. So, prepare yourself to embark on an exciting journey where we'll explore different CBT techniques to navigate everyday challenges.

Now, let's explore dialectical behavior therapy!

Think of DBT as the cool sibling of CBT.

Psychologist Marsha Linehan developed DBT in the late 1980s. Her inspiration was partly from her own experience. As a young woman, she had intense emotional struggles and even contemplated suicide. Over the years, her journey with mental health challenges gave her insights into the suffering of her patients.

Linehan saw the need for a holistic approach and wanted to create a therapeutic modality that would help people struggling with intense emotions, feelings of constant crisis, and self-destructive behaviors. So, she created DBT primarily to address the needs of individuals with borderline personality disorder (BPD), a condition characterized by self-destructive behaviors, emotional dysregulation, and unstable relationships.

The "dialectical" in DBT comes from dialectical philosophy, which emphasizes the need to balance opposing forces. In DBT, this means finding a balance between accepting who you are now and working to improve things that cause you distress. It's like you saying, *I am okay with being as I am, but I will strive to become better.*

Dr Linehan believes acknowledging and accepting your feelings, even when they seem irrational, is essential for progress. For decades, DBT has provided teens with the tools and strategies needed to control their emotions and lead healthier and more fulfilling lives.

DBT consists of four core modules: mindfulness, distress tolerance, emotion regulation, and interpersonal effectiveness. These modules encourage building different skills, including managing emotions and improving relationships.

Now, let's break DBT down a bit:

Mindfulness: This entails being aware of what's happening inside you and your environment without judgment. You'll watch your thoughts and feelings pass like clouds in the sky and not get caught up in the storm.

Change: Instead of sitting down and accepting everything that happens to you without acting, DBT encourages you to make positive changes in your life. It's like you saying, *I know how I feel; I can work on improving my feelings.*

Acceptance: When your emotions are overwhelming and uncomfortable, you want to push them away and not have them. However, DBT encourages permitting yourself to feel your emotions. Understand that having those emotions doesn't make you a bad person.

Balance: This means finding the sweet spot between accepting how you are and making changes to become a better version of yourself. It's like telling yourself, *I am a work in progress, and I can be better.*

So, there you have it! As we continue this journey, we'll explore different CBT and DBT skills and techniques to help you find peace amid chaos.

Now it's time for your very first exercise.

Costs / Benefits of Change

This exercise aims to identify the costs and benefits of committing to the changes you want to make on this journey.

Write the potential costs (negative aspects) of using CBT to improve your mental health in the left column. In the right column, write the potential benefits (positive aspects) you might gain from CBT. Be as specific as possible. Two examples have been provided.

Costs	Benefits
Difficulty confronting challenging thoughts	Decreased anxiety and depression symptoms
Emotional discomfort	Greater emotional resilience

Use this worksheet to determine whether your thoughts are helpful or not. It should give you an alternative way of thinking. The specific costs and benefits will be different for everyone, so make sure you clarify your personal reasons for starting this journey.

Many people start therapy without a clear understanding of the specific problems they want to work on. The following exercise offers a structured way to identify your problems and their related thoughts, emotions, and goals.

Here is an example of creating problem statements:

The Problem	I feel stressed when I have a lot of homework to do.
Emotions/Impact	When stressed about my homework, I become irritable and anxious and can't focus on other tasks. This makes me less productive and affects my overall well-being.
Thoughts/Beliefs	I often have thoughts like, "I can't do all this work" or "I'm not smart enough to do this."
Distress Rating (1 = Minimal, 10 = Maximum)	8
Frequency (Daily, Weekly, Monthly)	Almost every day.
Goals for Therapy	To learn skills and strategies to manage my emotions and stress, improve my time-management skills, and feel more confident handling life's difficulties.

Now, create your own problem statements following the example above.

The Problem	
Emotions/Impact	
Thoughts/Beliefs	
Distress Rating (1 = Minimal, 10 = Maximum)	
Frequency (Daily, Weekly, Monthly)	
Goals for Therapy	

Exercise 3 — Goals for Therapy

Goals are essential on this journey. When you set clear goals, you can structure your learning and track your progress.

This exercise highlights how to use the SMART goal model to challenge and reframe negative thoughts within 30 days. The goal should be Specific, Measurable, Achievable, Relevant, and Time-Bound (SMART).

Specific (What exactly do I want to achieve?)	I want to identify and confront negative thought patterns that lead to stress, self-doubt, and anxiety.
Measurable (How will I measure my progress?)	I will keep a daily journal to record negative thoughts as soon as I notice them.
Achievable (Is this goal realistic and attainable?)	Yes, it is. I will dedicate time to self-reflect and use CBT techniques to reframe my thoughts.
Relevant (Does this goal align with my values and priorities?)	It's relevant. I can achieve reduced anxiety, improved self-esteem, and more control of my emotions.
Time-Bound (When will I achieve this goal?)	Within the next 30 days with daily tracking.
Obstacles & Challenges (What can get in the way and how will I overcome it?)	Lack of motivation, procrastination, and fear.
Support Needed (Do I need support from others or resources?)	None since it's a personal journey, but I can always ask my parents for help.
Rewards (What will I reward myself with when I achieve this goal?)	A new pair of shoes.
Goal Status (Ongoing, completed, or abandoned)	Ongoing — this is in progress.
Next Steps (What will I do next to work on this goal?)	Continue reading this book and start tracking my thoughts.

Now it's time to show off what you've learned! Set your goals by filling up the empty columns below.

Specific
(What exactly do I want to achieve?)

Measurable
(How will I measure my progress?)

Achievable
(Is this goal realistic and attainable?)

Relevant
(Does this goal align with my values and priorities?)

Time-Bound
(When will I achieve this goal?)

Obstacles & Challenges
(What can get in the way and how will I overcome it?)

Support Needed
(Do I need support from others or resources?)

Rewards
(What will I reward myself with when I achieve this goal?)

Goal Status
(Ongoing, completed, or abandoned)

Next Steps
(What will I do next to work on this goal?)

Exercise 4 — Thought-Feeling-Behavior Connection

This exercise will guide you through analyzing a situation, considering your thoughts, feelings, and behaviors. The aim is to help you understand the connection between them and know how to manage them effectively.

Let's start!

Recall a recent event that significantly impacted your emotions and actions.
Use the space below to break down the event/situation into thoughts, feelings, and behaviors.

Let's start with your **thoughts**. Write down the specific thoughts that went through your mind during the event.

What about your **feelings**? Write down how the thoughts made you feel.
(Were you sad? Happy? Angry? Anxious?)

Finally, reflect on your **behaviors**. Write down how you reacted in response to the event.

Now, review the connection between your thoughts, feelings, and behaviors. How did they influence each other in this situation? Understanding the connection will give you insights into your reactions and allow you to make positive changes in your life.

Practical Examples of CBT And DBT

Enough of the theory! **Let's get practical.**

We can't deny that life is filled with twists and turns, throwing curveballs at us left and right. You might be excelling with your science practical or math, and the next day, you're dealing with friendship problems. Thankfully, CBT and DBT can be your trusted sidekicks that help save the day when dealing with your problems.

Here, I'll show you real-life situations and how CBT and DBT can help put your emotions in check.

Situation 1: The Big Test

Let's say you are in the classroom taking a test. It looks incredibly difficult and scary, and it's making your heart race and your palms sweat.

CBT can help you recognize that your anxious thoughts are sabotaging you instead of helping. CBT skills will teach you to challenge those negative thoughts, ask yourself if they are based on facts, and then develop more positive and realistic thoughts. So, in the situation of a big test, you'll tell yourself, *I've studied so hard for this test; I know I can do this,* and the test will become less scary.

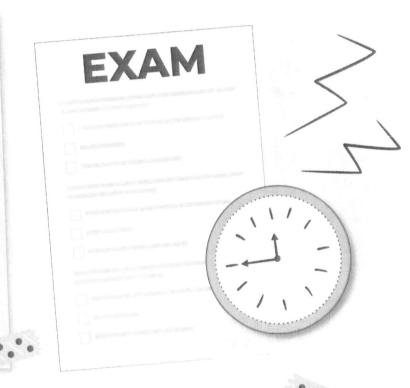

Situation 2: Awkward Social Gathering

You got an invite to a party. Getting there, you realize it's a huge crowd with no familiar faces except the person who invited you. Your social anxiety starts creeping in, and you're uncomfortable.

Here, both CBT and DBT are helpful. By using mindfulness and breathing exercises, you can stay in the present moment and not get lost in anxious thoughts about what has happened or will happen. You'll take a deep breath and focus on the people around you, reminding yourself that it's okay to feel anxious. Also, using a DBT technique called **half-smile** can help you relax your facial muscles and, in no time, start chatting with people.

Situation 3: Stress Monster

Perhaps you're juggling homework, house chores, extracurriculars, and the pressure of choosing a career path. This can build up into stress — a monster that creeps under your bed and keeps you awake at night.

CBT encourages you to identify the thoughts that invite stress and change them. Instead of thinking, *I am not good enough; I can't handle this*, think *I've got this!*

Situation 4: Drama

Arguments with your parents, misunderstandings, gossip, and conflict with your friends can get explosive!

CBT and DBT encourage you to acknowledge the connection between your thoughts and emotions. Don't react impulsively; take a deep breath and use the **Thought-Feeling-Behavior Connection** exercise to identify your angry thoughts and choose a more constructive response. A DBT technique called **willingness** encourages being open to different perspectives, which will help you keep your cool and resolve conflicts peacefully.

Situation 5: Peer Pressure

Have you ever looked in the mirror and hated your looks or felt intense pressure to fit into a certain group? Low self-esteem and peer pressure can be intense.

However, with CBT, you can challenge your negative thoughts and learn to see yourself as awesome, just the way you are. Read positive affirmations and self-love mantras aloud to boost your self-worth.

Mindful moments is a DBT technique that encourages you to stay true to yourself and make comfortable choices, even if you need to stand out.

These are just a few examples of how CBT and DBT techniques can benefit you. They can help you manage stress, boost self-esteem, handle conflicts, and navigate daily challenges.

So, don't be overwhelmed or sulk when life throws difficulties your way — CBT and DBT can help you kick them off like the champ that you are!

Exercise   5   Scenario-Based Quiz

This quiz aims to reinforce your understanding of when to apply CBT or DBT techniques in real-life scenarios. For each scenario, choose whether CBT or DBT would more effectively address the situation.

Questions:

1. Dealing with Exam Anxiety
There's a big exam coming up, and you're overwhelmed with anxiety. Which therapy is best to use?

    a) CBT   b) DBT

2. Handling a Heated Argument
You're having a heated argument with your best friend, and things get bad. Which therapy is best to use?

    a) CBT   b) DBT

3. Managing Negative Self-Talk
You are always criticizing yourself and limiting your abilities. Which therapy is best to address negative self-talk?

    a) CBT   b) DBT

4. Coping with Intense Emotions
You are going through a crisis and struggling with intense emotions like anger. Which therapy is best to manage those emotions?

    a) CBT   b) DBT

5. Building Communication Skills
You want to improve your communication skills. Which therapy is best for enhancing communication?

    a) CBT   b) DBT

Answers: 1. a (CBT) , 2. b (DBT), 3. a (CBT), 4. b (DBT), 5. b (DBT)

Exercise 6 — Reflect and Discuss

Use the following journal prompts as a starting point to explore CBT and DBT techniques. Ensure you engage in thoughtful self-exploration and consider the benefits of these therapeutic approaches.

1 Write about a situation in which you'd like to use CBT techniques to change your thought patterns and emotional responses.

2 Write about a recent communication challenge with a friend, colleague, or family member. How do you want DBT principles to improve your interactions?

3 List three examples of negative self-talk you often have.

4 Set a SMART goal (Specific, Measurable, Achievable, Relevant, Time-bound) for something you want to achieve. Describe why the goal is important to you.

Finally, CBT and DBT, though distinct in their philosophies, share a common mission: to empower us to take charge of our lives and build a better future. Stay with me, as we're about to transform your daily experiences in the following chapters!

Chapter 2

Unlocking Your Emotional Superpowers

Before we start this chapter, let's get one thing straight: you're an extraordinary teenager. See yourself as a superhero with the potential to unlock many powers, and this chapter will be the guide to help you reach your full potential by harnessing those incredible powers you have lying dormant — hidden with your emotions.

Picture this chapter as your personal superhero training academy. It will equip you with the tools and knowledge to master your emotional universe.

 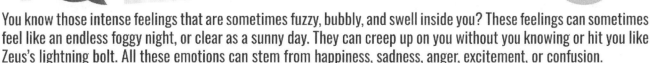

Understanding and Naming Emotions

You know those intense feelings that are sometimes fuzzy, bubbly, and swell inside you? These feelings can sometimes feel like an endless foggy night, or clear as a sunny day. They can creep up on you without you knowing or hit you like Zeus's lightning bolt. All these emotions can stem from happiness, sadness, anger, excitement, or confusion.

What if you had the power to know what you're feeling, like a detective? That way, you could make more sense of your world. For example, when you feel upset, you can slow down and ask yourself, *Why am I upset?* It could be because you are tired and hungry, or someone broke one of your favorite things. Understanding the "why" behind your emotions helps you respond better to situations.

As a kid, I'd imagine emotions as Lego characters, each with its own unique characteristics, personality, and superpower. I named my emotions and attributed each one to a Lego character. I gained control over my emotions and could use the powers of each character for good. Instead of thinking, *I feel scared and worried about the tryouts,* I thought, *I feel anxious about the tryouts.* Doing this gives you a clearer picture of what's going on. Let me show you a simpler way to name and attribute your emotions.

Imagine emotions are like the planets. Each one has its own unique powers and features. You can now attribute the emotions you feel to a planet. For instance, when you're upset, you can call it Mercury. You can even create more planets and name them after your emotions — that's one of your superpowers!

Labeling your emotions makes it easier to express them to others. A friend will understand better if you say, "I'm feeling down today," when you're depressed. Additionally, identifying your feelings by name makes it easier to decide how to handle them. For instance, you can use relaxation techniques when you know you're feeling anxious. If you're happy, you can celebrate!

In a nutshell, understanding and naming emotions is like having a map for your feelings. It guides you through the ups and downs of life, helps you communicate with others, and lets you choose how to respond to the world around you.

Exercise 1 Naming Emotions

This exercise helps you tag your emotions. The labels help you understand what each emotion does, why it affects you, what it means, and how it contributes to your life.

Instructions:
1. Choose one of the emotions you usually feel, like happiness, sadness, anger, fear, or excitement.
2. Write down the name of the emotion you've chosen. For example, "Happiness."
3. Imagine this emotion is a living character in your life story. Imagine this character has a job.
4. Now, describe the emotion and its job. What's its purpose? What does it help you do or understand? Write them all out.
5. Give specific examples of when this emotion performs its job. For instance, if you picked "happiness," you might write, "Happiness reminds me that there are good moments, and they are worth celebrating and to enjoy my little wins."
6. Now, flip the feelings. Think about situations in which this emotion, though good, might not be so helpful. Are there times when it can get in the way or lead to challenges? For example, "When I get too excited from being happy and celebrating, I lose focus and track of time."

Emotion	Happiness
The Job	Happiness acts as a personal cheerleader for me. Its purpose is to remind me of life's wonderful things and celebrate happy events.
Examples	It shows up when I accomplish something, feel fulfilled, hang out with friends, win, eat my favorite ice cream, or achieve something I've worked hard for.
Feelings Flip	Sometimes, though, it can be a bit too much and exciting, like when I'm trying to focus on studying, and it keeps nudging me to watch an anime video.

Now, it's your turn! Fill in the empty columns.

Emotion	
The Job	
Examples	
Feelings Flip	

Take a deep breath, relax your thoughts, and reflect on your writing. Does this emotion serve any purpose in your life, even when challenging? How can you use this knowledge to navigate your emotions more effectively?

Remember, every emotion in your emotional toolbox serves a specific purpose. Understanding that purpose can help you manage and work with your emotions better. It's like having a superpower decoder wand for your feelings!

Wheel of Emotions is a fun exercise in which you spin a wheel and explore different emotions. It helps you become a specialist who can identify and understand various feelings.

Instructions:

1. Draw a big circle on plain paper to make a wheel. Divide the circle into different segments, like a pizza, and label each with an emotion. You can start with basic emotions like fear, happiness, anger, disgust, sadness, and playfulness, or be creative and add more specific emotions like gratitude, guilt, boredom, or jealousy.

2. Give your wheel a spin. Whichever emotion it lands on will be your emotion of the day.

3. Once you've identified the emotion of the day, take a moment to reflect on it. How do you feel the impact of this emotion in your body? How does this emotion affect your thoughts and actions?

4. Express or represent the emotion in a creative way, for example, telling a short story or drawing a picture that captures the feeling.

5. Journal what you've learned about the emotion of the day. How does developing a better understanding of this emotion help you improve your emotional control and navigate your feelings in everyday life?

6. Explore the wide variety of emotions by spinning the wheel daily. The more you do this, the more you'll learn, understand, and appreciate the many colorful feelings in your emotional palette.

Example

Emotion Wheel I

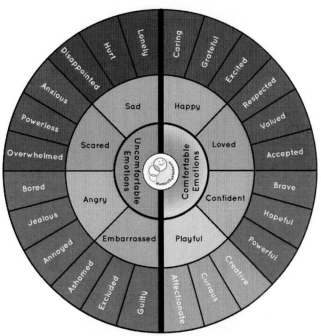

Source: Human systems (https://humansystems.co/emotionwheels/)

Spin Result	The wheel lands on "Excited."
Embrace the Emotion	Feeling excitement is like a bubbling energy that makes my heart beat faster, leaving me with a smile. I get pumped, motivated, and ready to tackle something fun or new.
Express It	I thought of a short anime story about an adventurer who embarks on an exciting voyage to uncover an old myth. I put myself in their shoes and described all the feelings of anticipation and joy.
Reflect	Today, I discovered that excitement is like a friendly jolt of energy. That fantastic feeling surges through me when I'm eagerly anticipating something special. What's even cooler is that it's contagious — it has this remarkable ability to spread to those around me, making them feel excited, too!

Now, it's your turn! Fill out the column after spinning your emotion wheel.

Spin Result	
Embrace the Emotion	
Express It	
Reflect	

This cool little activity lets you visually represent your emotions. It's like painting your feelings, and it can help you understand how they impact you.

What you need:
- Magazines or printed images
- Scissors
- Glue or tape
- A piece of paper or poster board

smiling faces

happy events

sunshine

Instructions:

1. Find a serene and comfortable place to work on your collage without distraction.

2. Consider the emotions you want to explore or express. You may select a single feeling or any combination of emotions that you have recently experienced.

3. Look through magazines or printed photos (you can also search and print images from the internet) for images, words, or phrases that symbolize your selected feelings. For example, if you're looking for images that represent "happiness," you can browse images of *smiling faces*, *happy events*, *sunshine*, or *joyous activities*.

4. Cut out the printed images and words you've chosen with care. Sort them into stacks according to the emotions they convey.

5. Begin arranging the cutouts on your paper or poster board to make your emotion collage. You can arrange them in any way that feels natural to you. Experiment with different layouts, colors, and sizes.

6. Once you're happy with the layout, glue or tape the cutouts to the paper. Make sure you firmly press them down to keep them in place.

7. Sit back and look at your completed emotion collage. What emotions do the visuals and phrases evoke in you? Do they accurately portray the emotions you wished to convey? Write your ideas and reflections in a journal or directly on the collage.

8. If you feel comfortable sharing your emotions, then go ahead and show your emotion collage to a friend, family member, or therapist. Discuss your work and the emotions you've experienced. This can be a terrific conversation starter and an opportunity to understand your emotions better.

Remember, you don't have to force things to appear perfect because there's no right or wrong way to create your emotion collage. It's all about expressing yourself and gaining insight into your feelings. So, relax and enjoy the process of art and self-discovery!

Exercise 4 — Emotion Journaling

Keep an **Emotion Journal** to write and record your feelings, the situations that trigger them, and your thoughts.

What you need:
 A journal or notebook
 A pen

Instructions:

1. Get a notebook or journal you're comfortable using.
2. You can decorate the cover to your taste or add quotes to make it your own.
3. Choose a specific time when you can always be free for journaling, for example, in the morning or before bed.
4. Always date your entries.
5. Name and write the emotion you're feeling.
6. Consider what triggers your emotion and write it in detail.
7. Consider the thoughts linked to this emotion.
8. Score the intensity of the emotion from 1 to 10.
9. List and describe how you usually cope with this emotion.
10. Write freely and honestly.
11. Track and analyze emotion, trigger, and thought patterns that you notice.
12. Acknowledge and celebrate your successes.
13. Conclude on a positive note.
14. Write consistently — it's the key to personal growth.

Use your Emotion Journal to understand yourself better and create good emotional behaviors. It's a journey of self-awareness and self-compassion. So, pick your journal, jot down your emotions, and grow!

Cultivating Emotional Awareness and Self-Awareness

Self-awareness and emotional awareness are some of the greatest superpowers residing within you. With these powers, you can face and navigate life's challenges, build long-lasting relationships, and embark on a journey of self-discovery.

Emotional awareness is akin to having a built-in radar for your emotions. **It is the ability to identify, understand, and describe your emotions.** Just as a good superhero knows their rivals' and foes' strengths and weaknesses, emotional awareness helps you get a clearer picture of your emotions.

You can understand the messages your emotions are trying to send to you if you pay attention to them. For instance, anxiety may indicate that you're confronting a significant challenge, whereas happiness may signal that you're moving in the right direction. Your decisions and behaviors are influenced by your emotional awareness, which aids in making sense of your inner world.

Now, let's talk about **self-awareness**. **Picture it as the secret identity of your favorite superhero persona.** Knowing oneself intimately and understanding one's values, beliefs, strengths, and limitations are essential components of self-awareness.

You can live a more fulfilling and authentic life by practicing self-awareness because it allows you to make decisions that align with who you are. This superpower can help you set meaningful goals, build healthy relationships, and overcome obstacles.

Knowing yourself and understanding your emotions are the foundations of emotional intelligence. They can help you:

- Take your feelings and values into account while making decisions.
- Strengthen your connections by having empathy for others.
- Handle the difficulties of life with resiliency and compassion for yourself.
- Establish and meet meaningful objectives that reflect your genuine self.

What if there were a remote control for your emotions, and a single click of a button could help you control how you feel? The **ABC PLEASE** exercise is your secret remote control to regulate your emotions effectively.

A — Accumulate Positives

This button helps you recharge your superpowers. Accumulating positives helps you think about activities that make you happy, content, or relaxed. These can include reading, listening to music, gardening, or spending time with your loved ones. The point is to accumulate positive experiences to boost your emotional well-being.

B — Build Mastery

Just as superheroes unlock their abilities, the "B" button helps you train and enhance your skills. Pick something you are good at and want to improve on. It could be a hobby, a new skill, a sport, or anything worth doing. Building mastery will help you gain confidence and control your emotions better.

C — Cope Ahead

Remember how Spiderman can sense danger and use his spidey senses to predict the best course of action to overcome challenges? Here, you'll plan for events or situations that might trigger emotions you find difficult to handle by thinking ahead about possible ways to cope with these challenges effectively. It's like having a plan to remain calm and focused to take on anything.

PLEASE: Physical Illness, Eating Right, Avoiding Mood-Altering Substances, Sleeping, and Exercising

The **PLEASE** acronym involves ensuring you're healthy, eating well-balanced meals, avoiding substances that may affect your emotions, getting enough sleep, and maintaining an active lifestyle.

The **ABC PLEASE** exercise is your secret remote control to effectively manage and regulate your emotions. The suggestions are like your superhero health bars. Taking care of your body will improve your emotions and state of mind.

It's time to get practical!

A — Accumulate Positives

List three activities or things that make you feel happy, content, or relaxed. These are your positive experiences that recharge your emotional well-being.

1. _____

2. _____

3. _____

B — Build Mastery

Identify a skill, interest, or activity you excel at or would like to improve. Give an example and describe it below.

Skill/Activity: _____

What can you do to work toward mastering this skill or activity? Write down your plan.

Plan for Mastery: _____

_____

C — Cope Ahead

Think of a situation you find challenging that might trigger difficult emotions. Describe it briefly.

Challenging Situation: _____

How can you handle this circumstance effectively? Make a list of some possible strategies or steps you can take.

Coping Strategies: _____

_____

PLEASE (Physical Illness, Eating Right, Avoiding Mood-Altering Substances, Sleeping, and Exercising)

Mark the ones you are already taking care of and note any areas that need improvement.

- [ ] Physical Illness
- [ ] Eating Right
- [ ] Avoiding Mood-Altering Substances
- [ ] Getting Enough Sleep
- [ ] Getting Regular Exercise

Practicing **ABC PLEASE** regularly can help keep you in control of your emotions and be in tip-top shape, just like a superhero does with their superpowers!

Exercise 6 — Mindful Emotion Meditation

This mindful meditation will help you explore and manage your emotions as you observe them without judgment.

Prepare a space:
- Sit or lie down in a quiet and comfortable place.
- Close your eyes, or if you prefer, maintain a soft gaze on something.

Focus on your breath:
- Take a few deep breaths by slowly inhaling through your nose and exhaling through your mouth.
- Focus on the sensation of your breath as it enters and exits your body.

Body scan:
- Slowly scan your body's sensations from the top of your head to your toes. Are there areas of discomfort or tension?
- Bring your awareness to any emotions you're feeling. You're only observing them; don't try to change them.

Label your emotions:
- As you gain awareness of your emotions, label them in your mind. You can say, "I am feeling calm," "I am feeling happy," or "I am feeling overwhelmed."
- Ensure you use simple and non-judgmental language while labeling.

Observe without judgment:
- How do each of your emotions feel in your body? Are there any physical sensations associated with them?
- Allow the emotions to be there without holding on to or pushing them away.

Focus on your breath:
- Gently bring your focus back to your breath whenever your mind wanders and gets caught up in an emotion.

Release and let go:
- Take a few deep breaths again.
- Imagine that you're releasing tension and negative emotions with each exhale.

Gratitude:
- Be grateful for your self-awareness and emotional exploration.

Now, open your eyes if they are closed. You can journal about your experience with this exercise.

Do you have any insights or observations about your emotions? How do they manifest in your body? Write them down.

As you practice this exercise repeatedly, you'll become in tune with your emotions and equipped to manage them effectively.

The **Opposite to Emotion Action** exercise is a **DBT technique** that will help you manage overwhelming emotions by encouraging you to take actions opposite to what you instinctively feel like doing.

You'll get to:

- Identify overwhelming emotions.
- Acknowledge what your initial urge was.
- Choose an opposite action.
- Implement the action.
- Observe the impact it has on you and the situation.
- Reflect on the experience and repeat as needed.

Example: You have an upcoming presentation at school.

Emotion	Anxiety.
Initial Urge	To avoid the upcoming presentation.
Opposite Action	Prepare thoroughly and face the presentation. Take deep breaths to make myself calm.
Impact	By implementing the opposite action, my anxiety was reduced, and my confidence improved. I was more in control while presenting.

It's your turn!

Emotion	
Initial Urge	
Opposite Action	
Impact	

Remember, this worksheet is a tool to help you manage overwhelming emotions. Use it as needed to enhance your emotional regulation skills.

Exercise 8 Feelings Check-In

This exercise aims to help you become more aware of your emotions, manage them, and improve your emotional well-being.

Let's get started!

Date: **Time:**

Identify and name the primary emotion you are currently experiencing.

Rate the intensity of the identified emotion on a scale from 1 to 10.

Describe the physical sensations you experience due to the emotion, for example, butterflies in your stomach, tension, a racing heart, or restlessness.

What might have triggered the emotion? Was it a thought? An event? An interaction?

Write any thoughts or beliefs associated with the emotion. What exactly is going through your mind right now?

How has this emotion influenced your behavior? Do you feel like avoiding certain situations? Communicating differently? Engaging in certain actions?

What is your desired emotional goal? Write what you want to achieve in terms of emotional state or behavior.

Outline a plan of action based on your desired outcome, for example, mindfulness techniques, coping strategies, or seeking support.

Reflect on your emotions and your plan of action. Are there other insights or feelings that came up during the reflection?

Exercise 9 Ride the Wave

Imagine your emotions as waves that come and go. This exercise will help you build resilience and cope with difficult emotions. As you unlock those inner strengths you will learn to navigate your emotional waves.

Step 1: Name your emotion.

What emotion are you feeling now? Write it down.

Step 2: Visualize riding the wave.

Close your eyes and visualize your emotion as a wave. Imagine yourself on a surfboard as you ride the wave — it rises, crests, and falls gently.

Step 3: Stay mindful of your breath.

As you ride the wave, focus on your breathing. Take slow and deep breaths, inhaling through your nose and exhaling through your mouth. The aim is to focus your attention on your breath.

Step 4: Observe without judgment.

Be non-judgmental as you observe the emotion. Notice any changes in your feelings and the intensity of your emotions.

Step 5: Reflect.

Reflect on your experience. Did you notice any changes in the intensity of the emotion? Did you gain any insights into how your emotions work? Write down your reflections.

Manage And Regulate Emotions Effectively

Before getting into the nitty-gritty of the techniques and strategies for managing and regulating your emotions, let's discuss why it's crucial to do so.

Our emotions can spiral out of control like wild stallions if left unchecked. This will create a chaotic ride, or in this case, rough teenage years. However, **you can achieve emotional well-being when armed with the right strategies**.

When you manage your emotions, you'll achieve:

- Reduced stress, and you can tackle life challenges with a clearer mind.
- Improved relationships, and you'll become a better friend and communicator.
- Enhanced decision-making and less impulsiveness.
- The ability to navigate difficult situations with resilience.
- Better self-esteem, which will foster a positive self-image and make you confident in your abilities.

Now that you've seen what you stand to gain when you manage your emotions effectively, it's time to get practical! Let's explore those exercises that'll help you get a grip on your emotions.

Exercise 10 The CBT Junction Model

Picture your emotions being a complex highway system with many twists and turns. In such a setting, you can easily get lost in emotional traffic. The **CBT Junction Model** can keep you on the right path.

This exercise will help you make practical and sustainable choices. On the left side of the model, as depicted below, identify unhelpful thoughts, behaviors, and avoidance patterns you may have. On the right side of the model, identify actions consistent with your purpose, values, goals, strengths, and opportunities.

For example:

On the left side, the thought can be, *I am such a failure for not getting into my dream college!* The emotion you feel at that moment can be *Frustration*. Your action/behavior can be *Isolating yourself from friends and family*.

On the right side, your goal and value can be *Pursue higher education and personal growth*. The action step, *Research alternative colleges and create a backup plan*.

?

Acting according to my mood, vulnerabilities or self-limitations	**Acting according to my purpose, values, goals and opportunities**
Unhelpful thoughts that I get caught up in, emotions that I struggle with, counter-productive behaviours and patterns of avoidance.	My purpose, value, goals, strengths, opportunities to try a different approach, things I can do to improve the situation and my personal wellbeing.
Unhelpful / Unworkable/ Unsustainable	**Helpful / Workable / Sustainable**

Trigger

Source: Think CBT
(https://thinkcbt.com/images/Downloads/Other_CBT_Resources/THINK_CBT_-_EXERCISE_6_THINK_CBT_JUNCTION_MODEL_V10.pdf)

Exercise 11 — Taming the APE

This exercise aims to provide emotional stability. You'll step back, notice your inner self-talk, feelings, and sensations, and reconnect with your environment or situation.

▰ Select an emotion. What emotion do you want to handle better? Write it down.

....
| |
| |
....

▰ Close your eyes and remember an event that brings you peace. Focus on your bodily sensations.

▰ Choose a simple action that feels soothing and comfortable to be your anchor, for example, touching your thumb and forefinger together.

▰ Associate your chosen anchor with the calm memory. Imagine it bringing serenity.

▰ Practice the anchor when the chosen emotion intensifies.

▰ Note how the anchor helped you. Did it reduce the emotion's intensity?

▰ Use your anchor consistently for emotional regulation.

Taming the APE is your personal tool to stay grounded when experiencing intense emotions. Practice it more often for better results.

Chapter 3

Conquering Your Inner Struggles

Have you ever heard a small voice speak to you? Telling you that you're not good enough or that no one would ever love you? Do you know what that small voice is and where it comes from?

Everyone has this tiny voice in their head. It's called **self-talk**, and it comes from your mind. Self-talk is what you say to yourself and about yourself, whether good or bad. You develop positive self-talk when you teach your mind to think positively about yourself and say good things about you.

Negative self-talk is when that voice in your head says bad things to you. It criticizes your every action and questions your every move. Over time, these negative thoughts become consistent and break your confidence and self-esteem.

Your mind is like soil — when you plant a good seed, water it with clean water, and fertilize it with manure, it'll grow into a healthy plant. However, if you plant a bad seed and poison it with weeds, the plant will rot and die. **If you fill your mind with good thoughts, there will be no space for negative self-talk.**

Let's talk about how to identify, understand, and tackle your negative self-talk.

Understanding Negative Self-Talk

Any thought process that keeps you from believing in your abilities can be classified as negative self-talk.

As a teen, you're going through a delicate phase in life, so you shouldn't harbor negative self-talk. It can damage your confidence in your abilities and make you feel like a failure. Focusing on negative thoughts can also lead to panic attacks, anxiety, and depression.

Negative self-talk doesn't just pop up one day and take over your mind. It starts with the little losses. For example, if you fail a test, you feel sad for the rest of the day. The negative thoughts prick your mind a little today and tomorrow, and by the next month, your mind is clouded by bad things. This is why cutting off all bad thoughts as soon as they appear is the best way to protect your mind.

Let's start with an exercise that nips bad thoughts in the bud.

Exercise 1   Self-Talk Journal

Writing how you feel about something not only relaxes your mind but also helps you explore why you feel that way and allows you to identify trigger patterns.

Your self-talk journal is like a storybook about your life and everything in your mind. In this journal, you will write about situations that happened during the day and how you reacted to them.

Get a journal or notepad to write out all your thoughts. **Write like you're talking to a best friend.** Pen down your experience with negative self-talk and how it made you feel. Pay attention to how writing about your thoughts makes you feel. For example:

> Today, a question was asked in class, and I was sure of the answer. I wanted to answer, but I was so scared. I thought I would get it wrong and everyone would laugh at me. My teacher told us the answer, and my answer was correct. I felt really sad for doubting myself. I was moody the entire day.

Your turn!

Exercise 2 Negative Self-Talk Quiz

Negative self-talk confuses you about your identity. You become unsure of your abilities and doubt your strengths. That's why having clarity is essential when combating negative self-talk.

This quiz helps you challenge your thoughts and identify what type of negative self-talk you struggle with. It will help you clarify why you act the way you do.

Tick Yes or No as it applies to you. Then, read below the table to learn more about your negative self-talk and why you think the things you do.

Questions	Yes	No
Do you...		
Compare yourself to others?		
Feel like you're not enough?		
Feel like a failure?		
Think no one would like you?		
Call yourself insulting names?		
Fear failure?		

If you compare yourself to others:

This negative self-talk is based on comparison. You constantly look at the lives of others and feel like you don't measure up. You think your life isn't glamorous enough, or your progress isn't as fast as your friends. To get rid of these thoughts, focus on yourself and getting better at what you do. Understand that your journey is different from anyone else's. Also, engage in activities you enjoy.

If you feel like you're not enough:

This type of negative self-talk is similar to comparison. But while comparison focuses on others, this one focuses on parts of yourself that aren't thriving. You might feel like you aren't doing well in certain areas of your life. You're always magnifying the bad side of things and ignoring progress. To eliminate this thought, focus on your efforts and your wins, even small ones. Focus on the positives!

If you feel like a failure:

You feel like one failure is a reflection of other parts of your life. For example, when you fail a test, you believe your life is ruined and nothing will ever go right again. Rather than focus on your failures, acknowledge that to learn and grow, you must make mistakes. To eliminate this thought, embrace failures and learn what you can from them.

If you think no one would like you:

This negative self-talk stems from a lack of acceptance. You're probably a people-pleaser. You want to be accepted and blame yourself when you're not. To stop these thoughts, acknowledge that you don't like everyone, and not everyone will love and accept you, and that's okay.

If you call yourself insulting names:

This negative self-talk stems from a flawed self-image. You think that you're not good at anything and have low self-esteem. You're constantly blaming yourself for mistakes. Understand that some things that happen have nothing to do with you. Train your mind to believe that good things may not come every day, but it doesn't mean that when bad things come, you're at fault.

If you fear failure:

You want perfection and to be in control, so when something doesn't go according to plan, you panic. To combat these thought patterns, accept that you can't control everything. Focus on what you can handle and learn from everything else.

The Effects of Negative Self-Talk

Negative self-talk often starts in childhood, but you might not realize it until later, when it becomes invasive and impossible to ignore. It begins when your family members talk down to you or you compare yourself to your friends.

The impact of negative self-talk is atrocious. The effects don't suddenly appear; they creep up on you until you're stuck in their grasp. They're like chains that take hold of your mind.

Negative self-talk can:

Break your confidence.

Negative self-talk leads to self-doubt. The more you tell yourself you can't do something, the more you'll believe it. You'll start feeling incompetent, and your belief in your abilities will disappear.

Lead to depression.

When you constantly tell yourself, I can't get better or I'm horrible, you start to feel frustrated and hopeless, which is a sign of depression. If you ruminate on these negative thoughts, you'll plunge deeper into depression.

Affect your relationships.

Negative self-talk makes you feel insecure. You start to withdraw from friends, communicate less, and become envious of your friends and their successes. These behaviors will affect your interactions and relationships.

Self-Talk Impact Chart

The following is a negative self-talk chart where you can write down your bad thoughts. On one side, write the bad thoughts; on the other, write how you feel and behave after these thoughts come. Two examples are provided.

Negative Thoughts	Your Response
I can't do it.	This makes me sad and I think I can't get anything right. I feel like a failure, and I abandon the task.
I wish I were like her.	When I think of this, I feel like nothing in my life is going well and that others are ahead of me. I try to act like the other person.

Exercise 4 — Personal Negative Self-Talk Assessment

Here, we'll assess how negative self-talk affects your daily life. Write out how you react to your negative self-talk in school, at home, or anywhere else.

Negative Self-Talk	Your Reactions
You're terrible at cooking.	I stopped cooking and went far away from the kitchen.
You'll make a bad artist.	I threw away all my drawing tools.

Identifying Negative Self-Talk Patterns

It's easy to spot negative self-talk patterns. Let's start with the easiest signs. What comes to mind when you're about to make a huge decision? Do you think, *Oh! I can handle this easily!* Or do you think, *I can't do it?* When you make mistakes, what do you think? *I'm a failure or I learn from my mistakes?* These are clues to your thought pattern.

There are many different cognitive distortions. The following are the four most common among teens:

Filtering

Have you ever thought about a situation and only focused on how bad it is, ignoring any potential good that could come from it? This is called filtering — when you only notice the negative parts and throw away the good parts.

For instance, at school, one friend compliments your handwriting and tells you how legible it is. A few minutes later, another friend notices that the edges of your book fold in and says that it doesn't look neat. Would you focus on the compliment the first friend gave or only on how old your book looks?

If you immediately forget all the good things because of one negative remark, you're filtering.

Personalizing

This type of negative self-talk involves blaming yourself for any bad thing that happens. For example, you planned a getaway picnic with your friends, but suddenly, it starts raining. If you assume the rain is falling because the universe doesn't want you to have fun, you're personalizing the situation.

Catastrophizing

This is when you automatically assume the worst. You're catastrophizing when you overreact to a situation, draw the worst conclusion, or believe that only bad things will happen.

Imagine your teacher is releasing the result of your test. If you automatically assume that you've failed the test and might have to retake the course without even checking, you're catastrophizing. Many people catastrophize because of past bad experiences or poor self-esteem. You prepare your mind for the worst so you don't feel bad if it happens.

Polarizing

This is an all-or-nothing pattern. It sees the world in extremes of black and white. There's no in-between. It's either yes or no, no maybe.

This kind of thinking is unrealistic. You force yourself to pick between two extremes. For you, the middle ground is off-limits. When you ignore the gray areas, you often experience negative emotions like impatience, bitterness, and disappointment.

Use the information above to recall instances when you've experienced negative thought patterns. Two examples are provided.

Negative Thought Patterns	Your Experience
Filtering	One day, my mum told me I was a good cook. She said that my fries were tasty and crunchy. But she also added that my sauce had too much pepper. I felt sad and focused only on the peppery sauce, ignoring the tasty fries.
Polarizing	I thought there were only two sides, success and failure. So, when I failed my test, I felt horrible. Since I had failed the test, that made me a failure. I ignored the part that I might be somewhere in between, struggling to get better.
Catastrophizing	
Personalizing	
Filtering	
Polarizing	

Exercise 6 — Traffic

Imagine that you're in traffic. You can see the cars driving past you and hear the tires against the road. Think of how the cars pass you by — that's how all negative thoughts should leave your mind. Acknowledge your thoughts, and don't judge or criticize yourself for having them.

Exercise 7 — Leaves On a Stream

Close your eyes and imagine yourself by a calm stream. The water flows softly, and the air is clean and fresh. Imagine that all your negative thoughts are like green leaves. Place each green leaf on the stream and watch it float away.

This signifies your negative thoughts floating away. It'll teach you mindfulness and thought diffusion. As you visualize these leaves floating away on a stream, create distance from your negative thoughts and let them go.

Cognitive Disputation

This exercise should be fun! You'll be a judge and put your thoughts on trial. You'll write out your thoughts and provide evidence for and against them. It's like being in a court of law; one lawyer speaks for the defendant and against the prosecutor.

At the end of the exercise, you'll decide, according to all your submissions, whether the thought should be thrown into prison or let go.

Thoughts	For Thought	Against Thought	Judgment
I'm not good enough to speak up in class.	Because I might make a mistake. Because my classmates would make fun of me.	Everyone makes mistakes. What if your classmates don't make fun of you?	This thought is false. Imprisonment!

Challenging Negative Self-Talk

Negative self-talk is difficult to cope with. Start by slowly reversing the patterns that caused you to form the negative thoughts in the first place. It won't happen quickly, but slowly and surely, you will be free from negative thoughts. The following tips will help you:

Become aware.

The first step to overcoming negative self-talk is to **admit their presence**. You must become aware of the thoughts, their triggers, and how they make you feel. Pause to reflect on your thoughts. Ask yourself, *What am I feeling*, and *why do I feel this way?*

Learn to notice when you're starting to think negatively and stop it immediately. Remember that you're only human, and it's normal to make mistakes, so **give yourself grace.**

Combat negative self-talk.

You're now aware of how and why you feel the way you do. Next, fight the negative thoughts. **Shut the voice up!** Know that these thoughts are irrational and untrue.

Use positive affirmations. If you think, *What if I'm not good enough?* fight that thought by saying, *I am good enough.* Train your mind to see the positives in all things.

Challenge negative thoughts. If your mind says, *What if the class laughs at you?* reply, *What if the class doesn't laugh at me?* **Questioning your negative thoughts reveals how unfounded most of them are.**

Practice positive self-talk.

The easiest way to get rid of negative self-talk is to do the opposite: **engage in positive self-talk.** Don't be so hard on yourself. **Talk to yourself like you would a good friend.**

Think of what you're grateful for instead of focusing on what isn't going well. When the negative thoughts kick in, **switch your attention to the things you love.** Keep a gratitude journal to remind yourself of everything you're grateful for.

Exercise 9 Theory A-B

This exercise will help you discover why your negative thoughts are still lurking around. In theory A, write about your negative thoughts. In theory B, decide whether your negative thoughts are from self-doubt, worry, or rumination.

Theory A	Theory B
I don't think I'm smart enough to pass a test.	This problem comes from my self-doubt because I doubt my abilities.
I think my classmates would laugh at me if I asked a question.	This problem comes from worry because I worry about what others think.

Exercise 10 — Clouds in the Sky

In this exercise, go outside and look at the sky. Imagine that all the thoughts in your mind are the clouds in the sky. Watch how the clouds in the sky move, and write what you observe.

Exercise 11 — Self-Compassion Mirror

This exercise will take you on a journey into your mind. It'll connect you to your thoughts, and you can directly tell your mind good things. Look into a mirror and say positive and kind words to yourself. Do it slowly and intentionally for a few minutes. Then, write out how it made you feel. For example:

After this exercise, I felt calm and stayed still for a moment. I felt satisfied with myself and powerful. There was a feeling of peace in my heart.

Exercise 12 Thought Detective

Let's play a game. You will play the role of a thought detective. Your duty is to fish out negative self-talk, challenge it, and reframe the thoughts into positive ones. You'll get one point for every negative thought that you change into a positive one. Go!

Negative Thoughts	CBT Techniques	Positive Thoughts	Points
It's hard, I can't do it.	• Positive affirmations • Journaling • Cognitive reframing	I can do anything I put my mind to.	1

Building a Positive Self-Talk Toolbox

Having a positive self-talk toolbox is something that every teen needs. In this toolbox, you'll have all the techniques to help you engage in positive self-talk.

Think of your positive self-talk toolbox as a first aid kit. In a first aid kit, you have all the instruments to care for an injured person before taking them to a doctor. Similarly, in a positive self-talk toolbox, you have all the techniques you need to treat yourself to a fulfilling positive self-talk session at any time.

Everyone is different, so there are different techniques in each person's toolbox. Each person will fill their toolbox with the techniques that work best for them. Here I've compiled a few effective techniques as exercises you can add to your toolbox.

Exercise 13 Positive Affirmation Cards

Create a positive affirmation card with affirmations that resonate with your situation. Take this card everywhere you go to remind you of all the good things in your life.

I can do anything I put my mind to.	I am smart and intelligent.

Exercise 14 Positive Self-Talk Art

Take a few minutes to create an artwork that shows your positive self-affirmation. This way, you're learning to dialogue positively with yourself. This positive dialogue will help you think positively about yourself.

Exercise 15 Be Your Own Cheerleader

The audience cheers for athletes during a run, which motivates them to run faster toward their goal. In the same vein, you need a cheerleader, too. It doesn't have to be another person. You can be your own cheerleader, cheering yourself to a better state of mind.

Here, you'll develop chants and self-talk mantras to fight off negative thought patterns. I'll share some of my mantras with you. You can say them daily to train your mind to believe them.

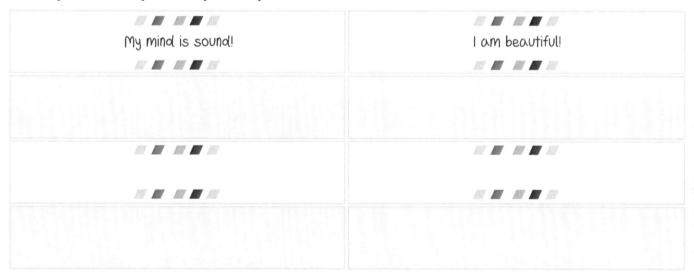

My mind is sound!

I am beautiful!

I've made mistakes all my life. At one point, I thought everything was ruined because of one mistake. However, I moved on from it. We've all had negative thoughts at some point in our lives. What matters is that we can move past them. Don't let bad thoughts steal your joy and confidence.

Fill your positive self-talk toolbox with happy memories and take it everywhere you go. It's the key to staying positive.

Chapter 4

Navigating Life's Challenges

As a teen girl, there were nights that I cried myself to sleep and days that I didn't want to go to school for fear of being laughed at. But I didn't let these challenges get to me. I carried my head high and acted like nothing happened.

My life would have been boring if I hadn't had any challenges. There'd be no fun memories to look back at. I'd have just been a girl who went to school and came back. Rinse and repeat!

Your failures and struggles are what truly make your story yours. They're what differentiate your journey from those of other teens. Everyone's story is unique because we all have different challenges that we've conquered.

Stop thinking of your challenges as problems. Instead, see them as the universe allowing you to write your story. What do you want your story to be? Do you want it to have a happy ending where you overcome your problems? Or will it show that you let your challenges take over and stop you from moving forward? **It's for you to decide!**

Common Teen Challenges

While every teenager's journey is unique, some challenges are common during adolescence. The following are some of the most prevalent:

Self-doubt

The teenage years are full of uncertainty. You're unsure about many things because you're in an important state of transition. You ask yourself: *Do I have the right friends? Am I making the right decisions? What advice should I listen to?*

Listen to yourself! Look inward. The answer you're looking for is in you; you already have it. If you continue to look outside yourself for answers, you'll never be satisfied.

Self-doubt creeps in when you believe that you aren't enough. You start questioning if you're what you think you are. *Am I good looking? Am I smart?* Never doubt yourself! Search your heart and discover who you are and what you want.

Academic Stress

School is a huge part of every teen's life. It's where you make friends and spend most of your time, learning and doing extracurricular activities. Because you spend so much time in school, it's bound to stretch you.

You come home with a lot of homework to do. You face tough exams to keep moving up the academic ladder. How do you cope with all these challenges? School is hard, but it isn't something you can't handle. Teens all over the world face academic stress. Keep pushing; you're not alone.

Peer Pressure

Being a teen means making friends and mingling with many people. Spending time with people can influence your thoughts and behavior positively or negatively.

When you spend more time with people who act right and do good things, you will start acting right, too. But if you hang around with people who cause havoc wherever they go, you'll be like them, too.

While I can't tell you who to spend your time with, ask yourself whether your friends influence you positively or negatively. Again, no one needs to tell you; the answer is inside you. Don't be compelled to do anything against your values to keep friendships. People come and go, but your values should remain forever.

Relationships

Your relationships greatly affect how well you function as a teen. I remember my first friendship breakup. I had a small fight with one of my friends, and she said such horrible things that I knew we couldn't be friends anymore.

After that fight, she apologized, but things never returned to what they were before. I had to move on from the friendship. I kept my distance from her whenever we were in the same space, which affected how well I played in volleyball games.

Have you ever had a friendship or romantic relationship that affected you that much? How did it make you feel?

Family

At this stage of your life, family is all you've got. Your family members are the first people you see when you wake up and the last people you see before you go to bed. You eat, play, laugh, and sleep together, so there's a deep connection. That's why any challenge at home will affect what you think, feel, and do.

Emotional Rollercoaster

Your body is changing during your teen years. You're growing and your hormones are raging. Your body is trying to interpret what your hormones want you to do, and this can make you happy or sad sometimes. Just like you, every other teen is going through this. Know that it won't last forever.

Social Media

Social media is a place to learn, have fun, and meet new people. However, for as many good and kind people there are online, there are twice as many unkind people. Some people come online to trick people and stalk them. Others get scammed of their money. You must be very careful with social media. Be conscious of the people you interact with and don't give out too much information about yourself.

Remember that social media is not accurate. Don't compare your real life to the edited pictures and likes on someone else's Instagram post. Be you!

Understanding these common teen challenges will remind you that you're not alone and that you're in control.

Exercise 1 Problem Solving

This exercise will help you identify your biggest challenge and produce a solution systematically. It makes the process of identifying, analyzing, and solving a problem easy.

Step 1: Identify the problem.

In this step, write down a specific problem or challenge you have. Attacking challenges one at a time makes it easier to find solutions to them.

Problem:

Step 2: Analyze the problem.

Think deeply and discover the cause of your challenges. Is it your actions or the actions of others? List possible contributors to the problem.

1._____

2._____

3._____

Step 3: Brainstorm solutions.

Think of potential solutions to your problem. Be creative and open-minded.

1._____

2._____

3._____

Step 4: Evaluate and choose.

Assess the pros and cons of each solution and choose the one that is most realistic and effective.

Chosen Solution:

Step 5: Make a plan.

Create a step-by-step plan for implementing your chosen solution. Break it down into small, achievable tasks:

Task 1:

Task 2:

Task 3:

Step 6: Take action.

Start taking the actions outlined in your plan. Begin as soon as possible.

Task 1:

Task 2:

Task 3:

Step 7: Monitor progress.

Regularly review your progress and make notes of any improvements.

Progress Notes:

Step 8: Reflect and adjust.

After some time, reflect on the effectiveness of your chosen solution.

⟋ Has it addressed the problem?   ⟋ Does the plan need any adjustments?

If necessary, revisit your list of solutions and try a different approach to see which one works best. After you find a solution to the first problem, you can try using this systematic approach for other challenges.

Exercise 2 — Pros and Cons

When searching for a solution to a problem, weigh the pros and cons of each. Doing so will help you make the most effective decision.

⬛ What decision do you need to make? Is it choosing what school to attend or what course to major in? Be clear about what you need to decide on.

Option A	Option B
I must choose a school to attend. My first choice is St. Ives School.	I must choose a school to attend. My second choice is St. Louis School.

⬛ What are the pros? There will be a good side to every choice. Write out the positives of each option.

Option A	Option B
It's not very far from my house.	The school buildings are spotless.

What are the cons? Just as there are positives, there are also downsides that come with your options. Write them down.

Option A	Option B
There's no free Wi-Fi for students.	It's very far away from my home.

After considering the pros and cons of both options, choose which is better. Assign a number from 1 to 10 to each pro and con to make this easy. Higher numbers mean it's a bigger deal and lower numbers mean they're things you can do without.

Add the numbers for both options and see which one has the higher score.

You might not make a perfect decision, but with this technique you'll make the best choice between the options you have.

Exercise 3 Challenge Journal

For this exercise, you'll need a journal. It will be called the Challenge Journal. In it you'll track your challenges and emotional responses. When you track your challenges and control how you respond to them, creating strategies to handle similar situations in the future will be easier.

What's the challenge?

Date: _____

Describe the challenge: (What happened? Who was involved? Where did it occur?)

Emotional response: (How did I feel during and after the challenge?)

Thoughts and beliefs: (What thoughts or beliefs went through my mind during the challenge?)

Physical sensations: (Did I notice any physical sensations, for example, tension, rapid heartbeat, sweating?)

Behavioral reactions: (How did I react to the challenge? Did I take any action?)

Coping: (What strategies did I use to cope with the challenge?)

Outcome: (What was the result of the challenge? How did it end?)

Reflection: (Looking back, what did I learn from this challenge? How could I have responded differently?)

Goal for next time: (If a similar challenge arises in the future, how would I like to respond differently?)

Additional notes: (Any other thoughts or observations related to this challenge?)

As a teen, you're faced with many activities that leave you moving from place to place, struggling to find your way. Amidst all the chaos, you can become oblivious to your immediate environment.

This exercise teaches you to be mindful. Living mindfully will help you be aware of yourself and face challenges as they come. **This exercise involves** three essential skills: observing, describing, **and** participating.

Observe

Go to a quiet place where you can be alone without any distractions. Close your eyes and slowly take five deep breaths. Pay attention to your surroundings. What do you see? What does the air feel like? Observe everything you can see and feel. Then, write down your observations.

What do you see around you? Describe the colors, shapes, textures, and objects in your environment.

Did you hear anything? Write down any sounds, both near and far.

What do you smell? Are there any scents in the air?

Do you feel any physical sensations in your body? Pay attention to any tension, warmth, movement, or tingling.

What thoughts are going through your mind? Write them as they come, without trying to change them.

How do you feel currently? Describe your feelings in detail.

Describe

Think about a time when you felt a particular emotion, for example, happiness, sadness, fear, or pain. Describe how it felt by writing as many details as possible. This exercise will help you gain clarity on your emotions.

Describe your situation or emotion. What happened? What triggered it? How did it feel?

Write down how your body reacted to this feeling. Did your heart start beating faster, or did your muscles tense up?

What was running through your mind during this experience? Write your thoughts down.

On a scale from 1 to 10, how strong was the emotion?

Participate

This skill requires your total attention and participation. You must fully immerse yourself in the activity to get the best results. First, pick an activity you do every day and participate fully in it by living in the moment. The activity could be eating, reading, walking, or anything else. Ensure that your attention is entirely on that action.

- Choose an activity you want to participate in. It could be something as simple as taking a walk.
- Take a deep breath and free your mind from distractions. Make sure you're entirely focused on the task at hand.
- Begin the activity with full attention. Observe each step involved.
- If you start to get distracted, gently bring your focus back to the activity.
- Complete the activity mindfully without rushing.

Reflection

Of the three skills discussed above (observing, describing, participating), **choose one** and **practice it every day for two weeks**. Document all your experiences and observations in a journal. Note the progress you made in your level of mindfulness from when you started the activity to the last day.

Did practicing this skill daily affect how you reacted to your everyday experiences? If so, how?

Did you observe any difference in how you interpreted your thoughts and emotions?

Talk about your experience, progress, and observations with someone you trust.

You don't become mindful of your surroundings by practicing these skills for a week and then throwing them away. It gets easier with time. So, be patient with yourself and enjoy the journey!

The Power of Resilience

There are times when everything will go smoothly for you. Other times, disaster will strike. Resilience is coming back stronger despite all the troubles that life throws at you. It's not something you're born with. Rather, with life experience, you can learn how to be resilient.

Life doesn't guarantee that the journey will be smooth. You will probably face terrible storms. Your health could take a turn, you may have to move to a new country, or your parents might get separated. **But none of these storms should stop you from doing your best.**

Exercise 5 Resilience Storytelling

There are people all over the world whose resilience stories have inspired me to do better. I'll share a few stories below:

Oprah Winfrey came from a poor family that could barely afford food and clothes. It was so bad that she had to wear dresses made from potato sacks sometimes. Worse still, when she was 14, she was sexually abused by her cousin, uncle, and other family members. Despite these challenges, Oprah never gave up. She worked tirelessly and eventually became a successful media mogul, actress, and producer.

J.K. Rowling was once a struggling writer who no one paid attention to. She sent her manuscript to many publishers but was turned down countless times, but she didn't stop writing and trying her luck. Then a small publishing company decided to take a chance on her, and now she's one of the most successful authors in the world.

Malala Yousafzai was once like any other kid. When she was 11 years old, she was shot in the head by Taliban militants on her way home from school for fighting for the rights of women and girls. Thankfully, she recovered and didn't stop fighting. Today, the world recognizes her as a symbol of courage and resilience.

Nelson Mandela spent 27 years in a tiny prison cell because he refused to accept injustice. After his release, he became the president of South Africa and continued to fight for freedom.

It's your turn! Search for stories online, in books, or in your experience that inspire you to be resilient. They don't have to be about famous people; you can think of a good neighbor or an honest leader. Tell your friends and family the story, and let it inspire you.

Write out lessons you learned from the resilience story you read.

Exercise 6 Wise Mind ACCEPTS

The **Wise Mind ACCEPTS** is a toolbox of distraction techniques that can help you manage intense emotions and regain control when facing challenging situations. Whenever you feel overwhelmed with emotions, take a tool out of this box and use it to distract yourself until you can find a solution.

A — **Activities.** Many activities can lift your mood or relax your mind, for example, engaging in a sport, calling a friend, or cleaning your room. **Just do what makes you happy.**

C — **Contributing.** I'm sure it's not just me who gets excited when I can lend a helping hand to others. Try it! You could volunteer, make a donation, or just provide a listening ear for someone who needs it. **By giving, you'll feel a sense of purpose.**

C — **Comparisons.** Remember that there was a time when things were much worse than they currently are. **Look back and think of how much you've overcome and how far you've come.** It's a great way to convince yourself that you can defeat any obstacle.

E — **Emotions.** No matter how much you try to ignore your emotions, they come bursting out anyway. So feel them. If you want to cry, do it. Vent to a friend or laugh. **Allow yourself to feel all your emotions.**

P — **Pushing Away.** If you're like me and don't like to address issues right away, that's fine. If your challenges are too much to handle now, put them away and come back to them when you can. **Focus on the now, not the what ifs.**

T — **Thoughts.** Your mind is probably overthinking things. Don't focus on what's going wrong. Instead, direct your thoughts to the positives, the things that are going well. **Give yourself some positive self-talk.**

S — **Sensations. Treat yourself to something good!** Satisfy your five senses with pleasant things, and your mood will improve. Sip a sweet drink, go for a swim, or sit in a place that smells nice. These pleasing activities will calm your anxiety.

Activities:

Write out the activities that most effectively distract you from your challenges.

Activity 1:

Activity 2:

Activity 3:

Contributing:

Write out ways you can help others while shifting your focus away from your challenges.

1. What can you give others today?

2. Is there anyone you can be kind to?

3. How can you lend a helping hand to someone in need?

Comparisons:

Imagine your past experiences. Remember when things were terrible, and you thought you'd give up? Remember how you bounced back and overcame those problems? Write down some experiences that you remember.

1. Example 1:

2. Example 2:

3. Example 3:

Emotions:

List activities that make you feel joyful, relaxed, or comfortable. These can help you change your emotional state when needed.

1. Joyful activity or memory:

2. Relaxing activity or memory:

3. Comforting activity or memory:

Pushing Away:

Are there times when you've temporarily ignored your problems so that you can return to them later? Describe a situation in which you might use this technique.

Situation:

Thoughts:

Create a list of neutral thoughts you can focus on when you need to take your mind off of distressing thoughts.

1. Neutral thought 1:

2. Neutral thought 2:

3. Neutral thought 3:

Sensations:

What experiences appeal to your five senses and help you live in the moment?

1. Sensation or experience 1:

2. Sensation or experience 2:

3. Sensation or experience 3:

In this exercise, you will curate your resilience kit. You'll be like a master planner, identifying and building on your strengths. You'll also identify your triggers and find ways to tackle them.

Step 1: Identify your stressors.

What's been stressing you lately? Whether they're big or small, jot them down.

My exam results.

Step 2: Acknowledge your emotions.

Next to each stressor, write how it makes you feel.

The Stressor	How It Makes You Feel
My exam results.	I feel scared.

Step 3: Set realistic goals.

Don't overwhelm yourself by trying to solve all your problems at once. Choose one stressor from your list and set a goal for how you'll handle it.

Step 4: Think of solutions.

Come up with ways to tackle the stressor you have chosen.

The Stressor	Solutions
My exam results.	• Read more. • Pay attention in class.

Step 5: Seek support.

Don't be scared to ask for help when you need it. Who can you turn to for help when things get tough?

Step 6: Develop self-care strategies.

List activities that help you recharge and feel better.

Step 7: Track your progress.

Keep tabs on how you're doing. Are you meeting your goals?

Step 8: Celebrate your wins.

Whenever you achieve a goal, pat yourself on the back and treat yourself to something nice. You deserve it!

Embracing Failure as a Stepping Stone

Hey, do you know what's cooler than success? The road that leads to it! This road, usually filled with bumps, potholes, and many detours, is none other than failure. Surprising, right? Failure isn't your enemy; instead, see it as a catalyst that propels you to success.

We've all failed at some point in life. Your favorite artists? Producers turned them down before they were accepted by the one who made them famous. Sports legends? They've missed shots before scoring their winning goals. Thomas Edison had over 1,000 unsuccessful attempts before creating the light bulb. Everyone has their fair share of failure before succeeding.

Never see failure as the end — see it as a stepping stone. Let's say you're just learning to ride a bike. You'll probably wobble, lose your balance, and fall. However, with every fall, you'll learn control, balance, and perseverance, and by learning these, you can adjust and improve. This is an example of using your failures as stepping stones to success.

The next time you stumble, remember that everyone has had a taste of failure. The iconic people mentioned above never gave up when things got tough, and you shouldn't either. **Explore, stumble, fall, and rise stronger. Each setback will bring you closer to your goals.**

Radical Acceptance & Turning the Mind

This exercise encourages you to practice **radical acceptance (a DBT technique)** and **turning the mind (a CBT technique).** It will empower you to shift your mindset toward positive and constructive thinking.

While feeling and acknowledging your emotions is okay, you can change how you react to them.

Part 1: Radical Acceptance

▰ What's bothering you? Write it down.

▰ Now acknowledge your emotions, no matter how uncomfortable they are. Feel and name them. Say them out loud.

▰ Accept the reality of your present situation without judgment. Understand that some things are beyond your control, and feeling how you do is okay.

▰ Now, say this radical statement: "It is what it is, and I can't change it."

Part 2: Turning the Mind

The idea is to shift your mind from distressing emotions and thoughts to positive ones.

▰ What can you control? This can include decisions, actions, or responses.

▰ What are the positive actions you can take to address the current situation?

▰ Does your action align with what matters to you?

▰ Now pause and live in the moment. Take a few deep breaths.

This exercise combines radical acceptance with turning the mind to help you navigate challenging situations with resilience.

Exercise 9 Building Positive Experiences

This exercise will introduce positivity to your life as you become resilient in the face of challenges.

1. Identify four activities that make you feel relaxed, happy, or fulfilled. They can be big or small.

Activity 1:

Activity 2:

Activity 3:

Activity 4:

2. Schedule the positive activities by choosing one from the list and doing it for the entire week.

3. After completing the activity, reflect on how it made you feel. What part of the activity brought you peace, joy, or satisfaction?

The positive emotions you experienced:

Your favorite moments:

Why it matters to you:

4. Record your positive experiences by writing down each activity's date, activity, and reflections whenever you engage in them.

Date: _____

Activity: _____

Reflections: _____

_____

_____

_____

_____

Coping with Rejection

Rejection is one of life's toughest challenges. Whether it's not making the sports team, not getting into your dream college, or being turned down by a crush, it stings like a bee. However, there are effective strategies to help you bounce back and move forward.

 Exercise 10 STOP

We've all been anxious, overwhelmed, or stressed out because of rejection. This exercise can be a game changer for how you cope with painful emotions following a rejection.

Now is the time to hit the STOP button! It's an acronym for:

S — Stop whatever you're doing and freeze for a second.

T — Take a deep breath.

O — Observe what's happening around you and how you feel. Is it fear? Anger? Frustration? Acknowledge and name the emotions.

P — Proceed mindfully. Carefully consider your options and think of what the best move is.

As simple as this exercise is, it's effective. It gives you time to regain control of your situation and make better decisions without acting impulsively. Remember, when life throws you a curveball, and you feel like your entire world is crumbling, **STOP**. Use it as your secret weapon to help you stay calm and make better decisions.

Exercise 11 IMPROVE

This exercise will help you reframe the distress that comes with rejection. Use the **IMPROVE** technique during challenging times to make better choices. **IMPROVE** is an acronym that stands for:

I — Imagery.
Close your eyes and imagine you're in a calm and peaceful place, experiencing all the relaxing sensations. Breathe deeply, allowing the soothing imagery to calm your distress.

M — Meaning.
Find meaning in your current situation. What can you learn from this rejection? How can you grow from it?

P — Prayer.
If you're spiritual or religious, you can pray or engage in a spiritual practice to bring you peace and guidance.

R — Relaxation.
Relax yourself by practicing deep breathing to release tension and stress.

O — One thing at a time.
Focus on one thing at a time by breaking your experiences down into smaller, more manageable parts.

V — Vacation.
Take a mental vacation by daydreaming about a place you enjoy.

E — Encouragement.
Be your own cheerleader. Use positive affirmations to encourage yourself and replace negative thoughts with positive ones.

Remember, it's okay to be told "No." Use the **IMPROVE** technique to regain control of your emotions after a rejection and make healthy choices.

Chapter 5
Managing Stress and Anxiety

The next stop on this journey is learning how to manage stress and anxiety. For many, emotions feel like a turbulent rollercoaster. If this is how you feel, know that you aren't alone.

Emotions like stress and anxiety may feel like you're strapped into that ride, unable to control the twists and turns. Sometimes, they may even make you feel like you're about to throw up your last meal. That's how intense and powerful stress and anxiety can be.

The good news is you can learn to take charge of the rollercoaster. This chapter is about learning to navigate the ride, hit the brakes, and have fun. Here, you will find tips and strategies to create an effective stress and anxiety management toolkit.

Everyone experiences stress and anxiety, although on varying levels. They are normal emotions, but they can become overwhelming if left unchecked. With the right CBT and DBT tools, you'll have what it takes to decrease the intensity and frequency of both emotional states.

By the end of this chapter, you will know how to assert control over your emotional reactions and cultivate resilience to handle adversity with improved confidence and a calmer mind.

Understanding Stress and Anxiety

Are you familiar with that tiny rush of adrenaline when you're in line for the newest release of your favorite movie franchise? Or perhaps a new video game you can't wait to get your hands on? That's your body getting excited and ready for the incoming action.

Contrary to popular opinion, stress isn't bad in and of itself. We all need some pressure for motivation. In fact, a little stress before a job interview or a test can amp up your performance substantially.

But like all things, stress is only good in moderation. If it gets extreme, it can spiral out of control like a rollercoaster with malfunctioning brakes. Chronic stress puts you in a constant "fight or flight" mode, meaning you always feel on edge. And as you might expect, the feeling isn't fun.

Anxiety is a combination of fear, worry, and unease. Just like stress, anxiety can arise before a major event or a change. You might feel anxious when meeting someone for the first time or starting at a new school. It's normal to experience anxiety, but when it becomes chronic, you must act before it wrecks your mental health.

Stress is temporary and wanes over time. In contrast, anxiety feels persistent, lurking even when there's no obvious threat. Imagine what it would feel like to be stuck in a never-ending line at the cinema without a movie. That's how anxiety feels.

It is important to learn to recognize stress and anxiety to prevent them from sneaking up on you and doing unchecked damage.

Common Signs of Stress

▰ **Increased heart rate:**
Have you ever run a marathon? Remember the feeling of your heart racing? That's a sign of stress.

▰ **Fast breathing:**
Stress causes your breathing to become quick and shallow.

▰ **Tense muscles:**
Stress creates knots in the muscles, making them stiff.

▰ **Uncontrolled thoughts:**
Sometimes, stress floods the mind with a whirlpool of thoughts, and makes you feel like you can't focus.

Common Signs of Anxiety

▰ **Constant worry:**
Anxiety places you in a worrying loop. You find yourself constantly thinking about existing and potential problems and trying to brainstorm solutions.

▰ **Sleep issues:**
Anxiety can make it hard to sleep or give you vivid dreams.

▰ **Physical changes:**
Sweaty hands, aching tummy, and voice tremors are all signs of anxiety.

▰ **Avoidance:**
If you find yourself avoiding certain people, places, or things, it could be due to anxiety.

Common Stress and Anxiety Triggers for Teens:

1. Peer pressure:
The need to create connections with peers, make and maintain friends, conform to social expectations, and fit in can bring on stress and anxiety.

2. Academic pressure:
Homework, tests, college applications, and high expectations from parents and teachers can trigger stress and anxiety.

3. Home environment:
Family dynamics, such as having an abusive or authoritarian parent, conflict, or divorce, are common stressors for teenagers.

4. Social media:
Unchecked online interactions, the desire to project a perfect image, and cyberbullying can lead to anxiety.

5. Body image:
Preoccupation with one's physical appearance and being compared to others can contribute to anxiety.

6. Relationships:
Conflict in friendships or romantic relationships can be a stressor and a contributing factor to anxiety.

7. Uncertainty:
Worries about college, career choices, and the future can overwhelm teens and trigger chronic stress.

Identifying stressors can empower you to learn healthy coping strategies to manage stress and anxiety while prioritizing your mental well-being.

We all experience stress and anxiety sometimes, and nothing is wrong with that. But if these emotions start interfering with your everyday life or preventing you from enjoying activities, it's time to learn how to deal with them correctly.

Exercise 1 The Big Picture

Wondering how stress and anxiety fit into your daily life? This exercise will open your mind and help you see the big picture.

What to do:

1. Get a notebook, journal, or the notes app on your smartphone.

2. Write down a timeline of the events that have occurred in your life from when you were young until now. Try to remember as many things as possible. Include the year or the age you were beside each event.

3. Next, **highlight moments that caused you great stress or anxiety**, for example, when your family moved to a new neighborhood or you changed schools and had to meet new people.

4. Now, write down your emotional reactions to each experience of stress or anxiety. Did your heart rate increase when you heard your family was moving? Did you try to avoid moving?

5. The next step is to **look for patterns.** For instance, did certain events trigger stress and anxiety more frequently than others? Are there moments when you navigated a stressful event skillfully? If you find any pattern, underline or circle them. Then, categorize them according to the situation. For example, maybe you noticed a pattern of anxiety in social situations.

6. What would you like to change about the patterns? **Setting goals can help you gain clarity.** Would you like to be able to manage stress during tests? Reduce anxiety during interpersonal interactions? Create a list of goals at the bottom of the page.

7. If you're comfortable with it, talk about what you've written with someone you trust. A close friend, parent, or school counselor may be able to offer helpful insight.

This exercise aims to open your mind to where stress and anxiety tend to arise in your life. Having this information is the first step in learning to manage both emotions like a pro.

Exercise 2 Symptom Recognition

As you now know, stress and anxiety have varying symptoms, many of which overlap sometimes. So, you have to be skilled at recognizing the signs to differentiate between stress, anxiety, and other emotional states. Cultivating symptom recognition skills is akin to developing a superpower for emotion regulation.

Below is a list of symptoms. Match each symptom with the right emotion: stress, anxiety, or something else. Label **"S"** for **stress**, **"A"** for **Anxiety**, and **"O"** for **other emotional states** in the blank space next to the symptoms.

Here's the table:

Symptoms	S/A/O
Racing heart	
Restlessness	
Trouble focusing	
Feeling excited	
Feeling overwhelmed	
Sweaty palms	
Messy thoughts	
Feeling calm	
Shallow breathing	
Feeling happy	
Butterflies in the belly	
Feeling in control	

Check the right answers below:

Symptoms	S/A/O
Racing heart	A
Restlessness	A
Trouble focusing	S
Feeling excited	O
Feeling overwhelmed	S
Sweaty palms	A
Messy thoughts	A
Feeling calm	O
Shallow breathing	S
Feeling happy	O
Butterflies in the belly	O
Feeling in control	O

Recognizing these symptoms can help you learn to manage your emotions. It provides insight into what's happening within you and helps you choose the right approach to managing stress and anxiety.

Exercise 3 My Stress and Anxiety Scale

This self-assessment is an excellent tool for identifying the roots of stress and anxiety and their levels in your life. Rate each area of your life on a scale from 1 to 10 and provide reasons for each rating.

Doing this can help you achieve self-awareness, which, in turn, will allow you to recognize the areas you need to address. More importantly, you can monitor your progress in each area.

In this exercise, **1** indicates the **lowest stress or anxiety level** and **10** indicates the **highest level**. Reflect on your triggers and rate them below.

Trigger	Rating (1-10)	Reason for Rating
Academics or schoolwork		
Family situation		
Hobbies and interests		
Social situations		
Health concerns		
Future goals		

Rate each trigger on the scale and reflect on the reason for your ratings. Do certain triggers amplify stress and anxiety much more than others?

Again, this exercise aims to give insight into the areas where you're experiencing the most stress and anxiety. It's a great way to recognize where to concentrate your management efforts.

The Impact of Stress and Anxiety on Mental Health

Chronic stress and anxiety can have devastating effects on one's mental health. Understanding their potential impact is crucial to ensuring early intervention and adopting healthy and effective coping mechanisms.

The impact of stress:

It's natural for the body to respond to difficult situations with stress. Unfortunately, chronic stress can cause debilitating mental health problems if unaddressed. As a teen, living with long-term stress can lead to:

Anxiety disorders:
Prolonged stress can lead to generalized anxiety disorder, social anxiety disorder, panic disorder, and more.

Depression:
Chronic stress often precedes depression. You may feel overwhelmed and hopeless and lose interest in activities you used to enjoy.

Physical health problems:
Long-term stress can contribute to headaches, digestive issues, and other physical health problems, as well as increase the risk of stroke and heart disease.

The impact of long-term anxiety:

Like chronic stress, prolonged anxiety is highly detrimental to physical and mental health. As a teenager, living with chronic anxiety may lead you to experience:

Isolation:
Anxiety may cause you to withdraw from interpersonal interactions and social situations, leading to feelings of isolation and loneliness. Eventually, this could lead to depression.

Decreased quality of life:
Anxiety can make engaging in enjoyable activities, pursuing your goals, or attending school difficult. As a result, it can cause a decline in your quality of life.

Substance abuse:
Sometimes, teens turn to alcohol or drugs when anxiety becomes overwhelming, which can lead to addiction.

Identifying symptoms of chronic stress and anxiety is necessary for intervening early and preventing adverse outcomes.

Exercise 4 — Stress and Anxiety Trigger Tracker

This exercise will help you identify your stress and anxiety triggers, which will make taking steps toward effective stress and anxiety management easier. Tracking triggers is most convenient with a worksheet, so here's how to create yours:

1. Create a table with four columns. Label each column with "Trigger," "Physical Reactions," "Emotional Reactions," and "Coping Strategies," respectively.

2. In the "Trigger" column, write down thoughts, events, and situations that induce stress or anxiety. A trigger can be anything from social gatherings to school tests.

3. In the "Physical Reactions" column, list the physiological sensations you experience when stressed or anxious. Examples include sweating, fast heart rate, and shallow breathing. Describe the symptoms in detail.

4. In the "Emotional Reactions" column, write down how you feel when stressed or anxious, like irritable, worried, scared, or sad. Be specific.

5. In the "Coping Strategies" column, describe what you usually do when stressed or anxious. If there are any strategies you employ, write them down. This could be unhealthy coping mechanisms like overeating or avoidance or healthier options like talking to someone, working out, or meditating.

6. Keep this table and fill it in whenever you experience stress or anxiety. With time, patterns will emerge between certain triggers and your physical and emotional reactions. That will help you determine whether your coping strategies are effective or not.

Below is a sample of what your tracker should look like:

Trigger	Physical Reactions	Emotional Reactions	Coping Strategies
Exam	Racing heart, tensed muscles	Fear, worry	Positive self-talk, sharing with a friend

You'll learn more about your triggers with the stress and anxiety tracker. That way, you can make informed decisions in managing both emotions. Understanding something is the first step towards controlling it.

Along with the tracker, having another journal to track your triggers and emotional experiences and how they affect your mental well-being can be incredibly helpful. Here's what your journal entry might look like:

Date: _____

Emotion(s) experienced: _____

Trigger(s): _____

Effects on my mental health: _____

Entry:

Write about an experience with stress or anxiety that occurred during the day. Include as many details as you'd like. Journaling is great for introspecting and understanding yourself.

Toolkit For Managing Stress

Stress is a common issue for teens, and learning to manage it is vital for your emotional and mental well-being. This section provides a valuable resource designed to equip you with effective coping exercises.

Exercise 4 PACE Activity

Emotions aren't static; they change throughout the day based on your experiences. To shift your emotional state or improve your mood, you must change your behavior.

The **PACE Activity** aims to help you plan and commit to activities that nurture positive emotional states and maintain balance. **PACE** is an acronym for **Physical, Achievement, Connection,** and **Enjoyment**. These four areas of life require balance for optimal emotional well-being.

What to do:

Write down a list of activities you enjoy or want to try in each area (Physical, Achievement, Connection, and Enjoyment). For example:

Physical	Walking, swimming, meditation, yoga, dancing, skipping, jogging, cardio workouts
Achievement	Learning a new language, taking a test, completing a school project, setting and meeting small academic targets
Connection	Joining a school club, playing sports, hanging out with friends and family, volunteering at the local dog shelter
Enjoyment	Listening to music, reading a novel, watching a TV show, practicing the keyboard

Next, set a PACE schedule. Think of how much time you can dedicate to activities in each category weekly and set it up in your calendar. Be sure to include a healthy mix of activities in all four categories throughout the week.

Day	Physical	Achievement	Connection	Enjoyment
Monday				
Tuesday				
Wednesday				
Thursday				
Friday				
Saturday				
Sunday				

Commit to the schedule and be consistent. Whenever you miss an activity, reschedule it for a different day of the week.

Tune in to your emotions before, during, and after each activity. Write them down in a journal or the notes app on your phone.

Review your journal at the end of the week and reflect on your experience. Notice if there are activities that impact your emotional state more significantly than others, and note any patterns.

If your PACE schedule requires modification based on your review, adjust it accordingly.

Exploring different activities and spending more time doing those that positively impact your mood the most is important. Remember that your experiences and actions dictate how you feel throughout the day.

By purposefully engaging in activities that make you feel good, you can be more proactive about managing your emotions and enhancing your mental well-being.

Exercise 7 — Relaxation Playlist

This one is highly personal. Relaxing music is subjective, so take your time when creating a relaxation playlist. Of course, there are songs that people generally find calming and soothing, but it's best to choose songs that you connect with.

A good way to create your playlist is to open a music app, such as Spotify, and look up "relaxation playlists" or "calming songs." Then, listen to different songs and choose your favorites for your personal relaxation playlist.

Exercise 8 — Diaphragmatic Breathing

Also called abdominal or belly breathing, diaphragmatic breathing can be an excellent strategy for relaxing your mind and body. It involves aligning with the natural rhythm of your breath. My favorite thing about belly breathing is that the effect is immediate. It can instantly calm and focus the mind, relax the body, and eliminate stress.

Here's how you can practice diaphragmatic breathing:

1. Choose a quiet part of your home.

2. Sit comfortably on a chair or the floor. You can also lie down.

3. Breathe in deeply through the nose and count to four.

4. Hold your breath to another count of four.

5. Breathe out slowly through the mouth as you count to six.

6. When you exhale, visualize the stress leaving your body through the breath.

7. As you inhale and exhale, notice the rise and fall of your belly. Place a hand on your abdomen and another on your chest.

8. Continue breathing in deeply and out slowly until you feel relaxed.

You can try diaphragmatic breathing anytime you want quick relief from stress and anxiety or to relax your mind and body.

TIPP is an acronym for **Temperature, Intense Exercise, Paced Breathing,** and **Paired Muscle Relaxation**. TIPP aims to change the body's physiological response to decrease stress and anxiety.

Temperature:

Change your body's temperature to reduce muscle tension and shift physiological responses. You can:

- Place an ice pack on your neck or forehead.

- Splash some chilled water on your face.

- Dip your face in a bowl of cold water.

- Take a cold shower.

Intense Exercise:

Try a brief burst of intense physical activity. You can do push-ups, jumping jacks, brisk walking, or run around your yard for a few minutes. Push yourself as hard as possible before stopping.

Paced Breathing:

Try a quick belly breathing session to soothe your nervous system. Inhale deeply to a count of four, hold for four, and exhale slowly to a count of four. Continue this paced breathing activity for as long as you need to.

Paired Muscle Relaxation:

Tighten your muscle groups as hard as you can to create tension and then release them to induce relief. Do not tense for over a few seconds before releasing each muscle group. Start from your toes and move up until you complete every muscle group in your body.

Use the TIPP skills whenever you're in a difficult or distressing situation. Explore the techniques and determine which skills work best for changing your emotional state.

Exercise 10 5-Minute Daily Recharge

This is your daily mindfulness activity. It's a great way to remain mindful throughout the day. Mindfulness is proven effective for stress and anxiety management, so this exercise can help you relax your mind, relieve stress or anxiety, and boost your mood.

Here's how to practice the **5-minute daily recharge**:

1. Sit in a quiet and comfortable place where you won't be disturbed, like your bedroom, the park, or a special cozy spot.

2. Turn off all notifications on your phone and set a five-minute timer. You may close your eyes or keep them open — whatever you decide.

3. Breathe in deeply through the nose to a count of four. Then, breathe out slowly through the mouth to a count of six. Continue this breathing pattern for five minutes.

4. As you inhale and exhale, focus on your breath. Notice how the air feels as it goes through the nose, travels down the belly, and exits again through the mouth. Pay attention to the rise and fall of your belly and chest.

5. Focus on your breath, and gently direct attention back to the breath if your mind wanders. Notice your thoughts and acknowledge them, but don't engage. Instead, remain focused on your breath.

6. Let go of fears and worries as you inhale and exhale mindfully. Ground yourself in the present moment and let the calm wash over you.

7. Once the timer rings, end your mindfulness meditation.

Before you get up, take a few moments to reflect on how you feel after meditating. Are there changes in your mood or physical symptoms of stress? **Practice this daily to relax the body and mind while boosting well-being.**

Daily mindfulness practice can significantly improve your stress and anxiety management skills, so make it a habit and use it to build resilience.

Chapter 6
Building Self-Compassion

The world is filled with people who act like saints, covering up all their struggles and pretending to be perfect. It's sad, but I don't blame them. They're only looking out for themselves.

Human beings are attracted to the colorful side of things. We only want to see the good parts of people and condemn them when they show their struggles. Everyone wears a mask of perfection to be accepted by society, and we're scared to be vulnerable because people are quick to judge.

Being a teen in today's world is challenging, but you're strong. **Search for strength from within** — the strength to give yourself grace even when others judge you.

You'll learn all about self-compassion in this chapter. It'll guide you towards understanding yourself, accepting your flaws, and giving yourself the grace to be the best version of yourself. **Self-compassion will give you the strength to face today's world. This strength doesn't come from hiding your flaws but embracing them and trying to improve.**

The Power of Self-Compassion

Imagine your best friend failed a test or got kicked out of the football club. What would you do to help him feel better? I assume you'd be kind to your friend. You'd speak to him nicely and tell him how he's such a great player, and it doesn't matter whether he's on the team.

These are acts of compassion. They show that you love your friends and want the best for them. Now, imagine performing these acts of compassion on yourself during down times. This is called self-compassion.

Self-compassion is like being your own best friend when things aren't going right. It means acknowledging that you messed up but refusing to remain in the mess that you made. You treated your friend kindly when he failed, but would you treat yourself similarly given the same circumstance? **You must understand that compassion doesn't always have to come from others; you can be self-compassionate.** And that is the best form of compassion.

You might wonder how showing yourself compassion makes can anything better, so **I'll tell you how!**

▰ ▰ ▰ It helps you de-stress.

I might be wrong about many things, but one thing I'm sure of is that teens undergo lots of stress. This stage of life involves stressful situations that might affect your mental stability as you go from playgrounds to classrooms.

By introducing self-compassion into your lifestyle, you teach yourself to accept that stress is inevitable. Knowing this helps you find a way around stress instead of dwelling on it.

▰ ▰ ▰ It keeps you motivated.

Knowing that your mistake doesn't define you will motivate you to keep working towards your goal. **Self-compassion stems from a desire to learn and grow**, so whenever you show that tender love, you feed your confidence and motivate yourself to improve.

▰ ▰ ▰ It reduces fear and anxiety.

Failure or mistakes are a part of our lives; they come and go. However, their presence can make you scared and anxious. That's why being gentle and compassionate with yourself is crucial.

Self-compassion will help you divert focus from the consequences of your mistakes and remain calm and optimistic despite the troubles around you. It'll keep you emotionally resilient and train you to handle your problems like they're no big deal.

This exercise will be full of good vibes. You'll need to take off the cloak of self-judgment and cover yourself with a kindness jacket. This exercise will focus on training your mind to be kind to you. **We'll build a mansion of kindness from the little kindness crumbs in your heart. Let's go!**

◢ **Have a journal:** Before you start anything, get a journal to write in. It can be a cute notebook or an app on your phone.

◢ **My Kindness Bank:** This journal will be your bank of kindness. In it, you will write down acts of kindness you saw or experienced yourself. It can be something as minor as getting someone a cup of water or watching someone help an old lady cross the road. Ensure that you write everything before the end of each day. For example:

> I held the door open for my brother because he had a heavy load on his hands.

Explain the act of kindness: Give a short description of your experience. Don't forget to include the essential details. Who was involved? What happened?

My elder brother went grocery shopping and returned with a lot of bags in his hands. I stood by the door and held it open so he could enter.

Describe your emotions: Think deeply about how this kindness made you feel. Did it make you happy and warm your heart?

I felt proud of myself. My heart was filled with joy, and even my brother was happy.

Reflect: Relate your kindness to self-compassion and resilience. How do these acts of kindness make you feel about yourself? Do they contribute positively to your sense of self-worth?

My acts of kindness made me feel capable of doing good things. It improved my self-esteem.

Update regularly: It's best to do this exercise every day. Focusing on kindness and doing it frequently will become a mindset rather than a random notebook exercise. Make it part of your daily routine!

Talk about your experiences: Share your experience with family members or trusted friends. Talking about kindness with others will share the good vibes with everyone around you and make you feel like you're not alone.

As you show kindness to others, don't ignore yourself. Be kind to yourself, too. Showing kindness to others shouldn't hinder you from doing the same to yourself. Rest when you need to, take breaks, and eat well. These are ways of being kind to yourself. Embrace positivity, and it'll improve your self-compassion.

Self-Compassion vs. Self-Criticism

Self-compassion and self-criticism are like twins that can never coexist; if you have one, the other must leave. Whenever you commit an error, you feel sorry for yourself, search for ways to correct yourself, or start sulking and judging yourself. This is what makes self-compassion different from self-criticism.

Self-criticism

Self-criticism usually feels like a voice in your head, pointing out every mistake and making every failure look bigger than it is. It makes you approach your mistake from a place of fear. This fear triggers anxiety, which distracts you from the possibility of getting a positive result from the mistake.

Whenever we criticize ourselves, we feel horrible about ourselves and assume the character of a helpless victim. Imagine you have a friend that's always screaming at you, telling you that you're horrible and hurling insults at you. Wouldn't you stay away from them? You should do this to your inner critic: Throw it away!

Self-criticism does nothing good for us, so we can discard it quickly. Don't give in to that feeling of fear and guilt. You'll feel alive when you welcome self-compassion into your heart.

Self-compassion

Think about your best friends and how supportive they are when you're sad. They hug you, and all your problems disappear. That's what self-compassion is to you. Self-compassion approaches your mistakes from a place of love. It lets you know you've made a mistake but can do something to redeem yourself.

People who are compassionate to themselves are less likely to suffer from mental health problems because self-compassion teaches you to value and treat yourself with love. It also trains you to love yourself from within and not always look outside for others' approval.

Self-criticism makes you gloomy because it focuses on your mistakes and failures. Self-compassion is like sunshine; it lights up your day and fixes your focus on the positives.

We'll experience feelings of worthlessness, incompetence, and insecurity if we constantly criticize and belittle ourselves. But when we have self-compassion, we feel safe enough to accept our flaws and make the necessary corrections to become better people.

Self-Compassion vs. Self-Criticism Quiz

Many teens don't know when they're becoming critical with themselves. This exercise contains a quiz to help you assess whether you're self-compassionate or self-critical.

It doesn't end there! This quiz will also help you reflect on your reactions to failure and find better ways to live.

Instructions:

For each of the following statements, choose whether you react more self-compassionately or self-critically. If it's **self-compassionate**, write "**A**." If it's **self-critical**, write "**B**."

Statement	A/B
During hard times, I'm gentle and understanding with myself.	
I don't dwell on my mistakes or hate myself for being careless.	
I understand that no one is perfect. Everyone is flawed, including myself.	
I set high standards for myself, and when I can't meet them, I'm harsh with myself.	

Whenever I make mistakes, I practice self-kindness by reminding myself that everyone makes mistakes.

When I fall short of my goals, I am unforgiving to myself.

I see my mistakes as opportunities to learn more and grow.

I'm always blaming and criticizing myself for my shortcomings.

I give myself the same support and kindness I would offer a close friend.

Whenever I don't meet my expectations, I judge and condemn myself.

Scoring:

- How many As did you get? Count them.
- How many Bs did you get? Count them.

Interpretation:

- If you have more "A" responses, you have more self-compassion.
- If you have more "B" responses, you are more self-critical.

This exercise will teach you to treat yourself as tenderly as a wounded rabbit. Do it as frequently as possible to evaluate your progress. If the result shows you're more self-critical, please be gentle. It's okay to make mistakes as long as you can rise and learn from them.

Exercise 3 — Mindful Nature Adventure

This exercise is adventurous. It encourages you to leave your room and go out into nature. Choose a day to do this exercise. On your chosen day, **go on a nature adventure and practice mindfulness.**

Take note of nature's beauty and write down your encounter and how it connects you to your inner resilience and self-compassion.

Activity Date: _____

Location: _____

Instructions:

1. Choose a place that shows the beauty of nature, like a garden, park, or beach.

2. Choose a start and finish time so you don't get carried away. Your chosen time should be at least 30 minutes and not more than an hour.

3. As you start this exercise, be mindful. Be sensitive to all the elements of nature around you. Their colors, the sounds they make, how they smell and feel — take note of it all.

4. Find a comfortable spot to sit or stand. Then, take a few deep breaths to bring yourself to the present moment.

5. Notice the natural world around you. Pay attention to the details and beauty in everything you see and experience.

6. Use the spaces below to document your observations during your adventure. What did you see? How did you feel? Does nature have a smell?

Observations:

Describe what you see around you. What are the colors in the scenery? What does the grass feel like? Can you see any strange insects?

What sounds do you hear in this natural setting? The wind? Birds chirping?you see any strange insects?

Close your eyes so you can concentrate. What can you smell? Is there a gentle breeze or other tactile sensations?

Reflection:

What do you feel as you experience these sensations? Does it have any effect on your mind? Do you feel more connected to nature and yourself?

Do you know that nature also experiences growth, change, and challenges like you? Think about how nature survives change and how that teaches you to have resilience and self-compassion.

What did this adventure with nature teach you about yourself and your capacity for resilience?

After this exercise, you will feel recharged to continue towards your goal and be self-compassionate. Reflect on your own experiences and nurture your self-compassion and resilience.

Embracing Imperfection

I believe that there's no such thing as perfection. Every person or thing in this world has a flaw. **We have unique strengths and flaws that make us who we are.** I can sing beautifully, but I'm terrible at dancing. On the other hand, my brother is terrible at singing but dances beautifully. It would be absurd to forget how well I sing and focus on the fact that I can't dance, so let's stop focusing on our flaws at the expense of our strengths. **Let us embrace our imperfections and look for ways to improve.**

Letting Go of Perfectionism

We all want everything to go just right sometimes. We want perfect grades, a perfect dress, or a haircut that's 10/10. That's perfectionism — and while it might seem like a good thing, it isn't. Perfectionism raises your expectations so high that your hopes come crashing down if anything goes wrong, leaving you sad and discouraged.

It's okay to want things to go right, but expecting perfection is too much. **Let it go!** You'll feel free when you let go of perfectionism and accept that things could go haywire at any time.

Celebrating Your Flaws as Strengths

I want you to look around and try to think of one person who doesn't have a flaw or bad habit they struggle with. I bet you can't! **Every human being is a combination of their strengths, flaws, and past mistakes.**

The flaws you see in yourself are not just "bad things;" they're features that make you who you are. So, don't hide them. Show your flaws while making moves to correct them.

Navigating Social Pressures with Grace

Going through high school comes with lots of pressure. You feel you need to look and act a certain way to be accepted. Parents expect you to have the best grades while excelling at sports and volunteering. The expectations placed on you are heavy!

These are all activities that you can successfully engage in, but make sure that whatever you do is for you. Put yourself first and make sure you're not burning yourself out to make another person happy. **You are who you are, so wear your crown and don't dim your light for another person to shine.**

Exercise 4 — Self-Compassion Letter

If you could meet your favorite celebrity, you'd say many nice things to them. You are your favorite person, so say sweet things to yourself, too. You deserve all the love and kindness you have to give. In this exercise you will write a beautiful letter to yourself. Doing so will increase your self-compassion and boost your resilience.

1. **Set the scene:** Go to a quiet and comfortable spot where you won't be distracted.

2. **Address your hero:** Start your letter with "Dear [Your Name], my superhero self." Starting your letter this way evokes a feeling of powerful self-love and compassion.

3. **Express yourself:** Think deeply and start writing from your heart. Accept your struggles and let your emotions flow onto the page.

4. **Be kind and supportive:** As you write down all the thoughts of your heart, don't be harsh to yourself. Instead, write kind words of understanding and encouragement. To make it easier, imagine that you're speaking to your best friend who's struggling. What would you tell them?

5. **Share your resilience:** Think about when you were strong and resilient. Be proud of those moments!

6. **Encourage growth:** Sometimes growth requires pain. Embrace your painful growth and think of your imperfections as opportunities to improve. Remember, every scar tells a story of healing and strength.

7. **Self-compassion boosters:** Write down positive affirmations that trigger thoughts of self-compassion. Remind yourself that you are worthy of love and understanding.

8. **End with love:** Sign your letter with love and admiration for the fantastic person you are.

Dear .... my superhero self.

My Positive Affirmations:

 With love and admiration,

Exercise 5 Affirmations Tower

Life won't always be smooth. There will be good times and some bad times, too. This exercise requires you to build a tower of affirmations to fall back on whenever life gets tough. It will remind you of your resilience and self-compassion and encourage you not to give up when the going gets tough. Share a picture of your tower and the affirmations that inspire you.

Instructions:

1. Gather sticky notes, index cards, or small pieces of paper and colorful pens or crayons.

2. Next, think about all the affirmations that inspire you. Search for affirmations online that make you feel better and write each on a sticky note or piece of paper.

3. Stack the affirmation notes on each other to build a tower.

4. Take a picture of your affirmations tower once it's complete and keep it safe.

5. Share your affirmations tower with someone you trust.

My Affirmations:

1. _____

2. _____

3. _____

4. _____

5. _____

My Affirmations:

6. _____

7. _____

8. _____

9. _____

10. _____

Here are some affirmations to get you started:

1. I am resilient and can overcome any challenge.

2. I give myself all the love and kindness I deserve.

3. I embrace my imperfections because they're a part of me that makes me unique.

4. I don't give up because I can handle whatever comes my way.

5. I am a work in progress, and that's perfectly okay.

These affirmations will guide you toward creating your personalized affirmations. Feel free to add them to your list or use them as inspiration.

Practical Exercises and Techniques for Building Self-Compassion

This is the best part of this chapter. Here, I won't be saying any boring stuff. We'll get down to doing practical exercises and techniques. These exercises will improve your self-compassion game by a great deal.

 Exercise   6   Loving Kindness

This exercise will teach you mindfulness and increase your love and compassion for yourself and others.

Instructions:

1. Ensure you're in a calm and quiet place where you won't be distracted.

2. Take 10 deep breaths to brace yourself.

3. Loving-kindness involves sending love and compassion to yourself and others. What do you think about loving kindness? How can you show loving kindness to yourself and others?

4. Use the space below to write your loving kindness wishes. Start with yourself and then extend them to others.

Loving Kindness Wishes:

① For Myself: Write a kind wish for yourself. Say, "May I remain happy and be at peace."

(2) **For a Loved One:** Think of someone close to you and send them a wish. Write, "May [Name] be healthy and successful."

(3) **For a Random Person:** Consider someone you're not close to, like a neighbor or classmate. Send them a wish of peace, like, "May [Name] be at peace."

(4) **For a Difficult Person:** Try to recall someone you've had a fallout with. Send them a wish, saying, "May [Name] find joy and peace."

(5) **For Everyone:** Share your wishes, saying, "May people everywhere be happy and healthy."

Now that you've written these wishes, how do you feel? Did wishing others well make you feel good about yourself and happy for others? Do you think doing this exercise regularly will help you be more self-compassionate?

Exercise 7 Gratitude Tree

Being thankful is an effective way to cultivate self-compassion in our minds. That's why having a gratitude tree is important. In this exercise, you'll create and reflect upon your gratitude tree and observe how it improves your self-compassion.

Instructions:

Go to a quiet place free from distraction. Take slow, deep breaths, then imagine a beautiful tree with branches and leaves. Then write or draw something you're grateful for on each leaf.

Leaf 1:
Describe or draw what you're grateful for.

Leaf 2:
Describe or draw what you're grateful for.

Leaf 3:
Describe or draw what you're grateful for.

Leaf 4:
Describe or draw what you're grateful for.

Leaf 5:
Describe or draw what you're grateful for.

After creating your gratitude tree, reflect on the positive feelings it creates. How does being grateful improve your sense of self-compassion and resilience?

Self-compassion is not something you practice for two weeks and throw away. It's an ongoing journey. And while you might fail at it sometimes, make sure you get back up and continue your journey. **Continue loving and being kind and gracious to yourself and others.**

Chapter 7

Building Healthy Relationships

Every day, we see people everywhere: on the bus, in the walkway, at school. Our lives are centered around relationships, who we meet, and how we relate to them. **Relationships are important.** Sometimes, they're pleasant; other times, they give us a heartache. Either way, the importance of healthy relationships cannot be overlooked.

Having relationships isn't about speaking to someone for 20 hours a day or going to the mall with someone every weekend. It means connecting with people in a way that benefits both parties. So, be willing to communicate, learn, and explore the personalities of others.

This chapter will cover what it means to have friends and form healthy relationships.

The Foundation of Healthy Relationships

A healthy relationship will provide emotional support and encourage personal growth.

I've watched people in **healthy relationships** closely, and I've found **four things** that are always present: **mutual respect, communication, trust,** and **partnership**. Without these, any relationship will crumble!

Respect:

In a healthy relationship, everyone is respected. Respect people's choices and treat them with love, empathy, and respect.

Effective communication:

Talking about how you feel and what you think in a relationship is important. Be honest and open about your choices and listen actively to others when they speak about their feelings.

Trust:

Without trust, you cannot love genuinely. Trust people's words and actions, and earn their trust by speaking the truth and having good intentions towards them.

Personal growth:

In a healthy relationship, both people are bound to grow and progress in their fields of interest. You support each other to be disciplined and achieve your goals.

Recognizing Red Flags

There are signs that can show when a relationship is toxic, and they're called red flags. A red flag signals danger. A relationship with red flags is one that is unhealthy or abusive, so run to safety. Some examples of red flags include:

Controlling behavior:

If your friend is bent on controlling your actions, decisions, and interactions with others, that's a red flag! Your relationship should not isolate you or stop you from relating with other friends or family.

Verbal or physical abuse:

Any relationship that involves insults, threats, or violence is unhealthy. If your friend makes you doubt yourself, that's a red flag!

Disregard for boundaries:

Boundaries should be respected in every relationship. The relationship is unhealthy if you cross each other's boundaries.

Lack of empathy:

Part of what makes us human is our ability to feel the pain of others. If someone refuses to understand your feelings, your relationship is unhealthy.

Setting Boundaries for Respectful Connections

In every relationship, it's important to have boundaries. Boundaries help to guide your actions and reactions as you relate with people. Here are some helpful tips for setting and maintaining boundaries in a healthy relationship:

Know your boundaries:
How can you communicate your boundaries effectively if you don't know them? Think deeply about things that make you uncomfortable in a relationship.

Communicate clearly:
Be willing to talk about how you feel. Express yourself clearly, assertively, and respectfully.

Stick to your boundaries:
If after communicating your boundaries, they're not respected, don't waver. Stick to your boundaries and be prepared to end the relationship if nothing changes.

Trust yourself:
Our mind knows when something isn't right, so **listen to your guts**. If you feel weird about something, speak up.

Support each other:
Be willing to respect another's boundaries as they have respected yours. Encourage yourselves to stick to your decisions and respect each other.

To enjoy respectful and healthy relationships, set and maintain boundaries. This will ensure the relationship has safety, trust, and understanding.

Healthy vs. Unhealthy Relationships Quiz

This exercise will make you think deeply and show you the difference between healthy and unhealthy relationships.

Scenario	Healthy or Unhealthy?
When you feel down, your friend listens closely and gives you support.	
Your friend doesn't want to spend time with you and is constantly canceling plans.	
Your friend respects your boundaries and doesn't make you do things you're uncomfortable with.	
Your friend always makes fun of your decisions, style, or hobbies.	
Your friend cheers you on, encourages your growth, and celebrates your achievements.	
Your friend gossips about you and spreads rumors when you're not around.	
When things are hard, your friend is there for you, and you return the favor	

Quiz Answers: 1. Healthy, 2. Unhealthy, 3. Healthy, 4. Unhealthy, 5. Healthy, 6. Unhealthy, 7. Healthy

Exercise 2 Submissive, Assertive & Aggressive Communication

There are three kinds of behaviors: submissive, assertive, and aggressive. This exercise will help you differentiate between them and teach you to communicate your needs assertively.

Instructions:

1. Submissive communication:
Recall when you were coerced into agreeing to something even when you didn't want to. Describe what happened.

2. Aggressive communication:
Think back to a situation in which you or a loved one used aggressive behavior during a fight. Describe the aggressive actions and what they led to.

3. Assertive communication:
Talk about when you or a loved one used assertive communication to set boundaries. Explain the situation and the assertive behaviors.

4. Self-assessment:

Based on your responses, which communication style do you use the most? Is there anything you want to change?

5. Roleplaying:

To practice assertive communication, pick a trustworthy family member or friend and roleplay until you can confidently communicate your wants and boundaries.

Examples:

Submissive: Your friend asks you to come with them to a club. You don't feel comfortable following them, but you do as they say because you don't want to let them down.

Aggressive: You and your classmate got into an argument about a group project. You screamed and said awful things.

Assertive: You need your notes for an upcoming exam, but your friend wants to borrow them for a class. You politely explain and refer her to another person.

Communicating your needs assertively is a necessary skill for developing healthy relationships. So, use this activity to practice your communication style.

Effective Communication Skills

To build and maintain successful relationships, teens need to communicate effectively. Effective communication is essential for building trust and connection in a relationship. You'll need communication skills like active listening, assertiveness, and open dialogue.

1. Active listening:

Active listening is more than just hearing words; it means completely interacting with what the other person is saying. Here's why active listening is so important:

- **Better understanding:** When you actively listen, you can better understand what the other person thinks and feels.

- **Validation:** Actively listening when someone speaks shows that you respect their opinions. It'll make them feel valued.

- **Conflict resolution:** When you listen actively, you can solve conflicts and reach a solution quickly.

- **Trust building:** Active listening builds trust in a relationship by showing willingness to participate and sympathize.

To actively listen, focus on the speaker and avoid distractions. Maintain eye contact and ask questions to show you understand what they say. Use your body language to indicate your attention by nodding when necessary.

2. Assertiveness:

This means how well you can express your thoughts, feelings, and needs in a straightforward manner that's not rude. You need this skill to maintain healthy relationships. You should practice assertiveness in your relationships for the following reasons:

Effective expression: When you actively listen, you can better understand what the other person thinks and feels.

Respectful communication: Respect is paramount. Assertiveness shows that you respect not only yourself but the other person also, which will help you keep a balanced dynamic.

Problem resolution: This skill is important when it comes to resolving problems because it allows for more open and honest communication, leading to effective solutions.

Stress reduction: Communicating assertively reduces stress because anxiety can begin to grow when things remain unsaid.

Using "I" statements is a helpful way to practice assertiveness and express your feelings. While doing this, try to avoid being aggressive. Focus on your message and remain respectful.

3. Open dialogue:

Open dialogue occurs when transparent discussions take place, which are vital for maintaining healthy relationships. Why should you practice open dialogue?

Conflict resolution: Open dialogue allows conflicts and disputes to be resolved amicably.

Trust and vulnerability: When discussions are transparent, trust and vulnerability will naturally flow. Open dialogue creates a safe atmosphere for individuals to share their thoughts and emotions.

Mutual growth: Individuals involved in an open dialogue will experience mutual growth because they can learn from each other. This goes a long way in helping the relationship.

Reduced misunderstandings: Open dialogue reduces the occurrences of assumptions because all parties involved are open about their feelings, so everyone knows how everyone feels.

To get the best out of open dialogue, individuals must be in an atmosphere where they feel safe and have no fear of being judged. This will help them open up and have more honest discussions.

Effective communication is vital in building healthy relationships with the people around us. Essential skills like active listening, assertiveness, and open dialogue promote understanding, conflict resolution, trust, and mutual growth. Mastering these skills will help you nurture better relationships.

Exercise 3 DEAR MAN

The **DEAR MAN** tool will improve your assertive communication skills. When you constantly practice it, you will become more confident in expressing yourself and better at maintaining fantastic relationships.

Step 1: Describe the scenario.

Think of a specific scenario in which you must communicate your needs and boundaries. Write a brief description of the scenario.

Step 2: Use the DEAR MAN script.

Use the DEAR MAN script to structure your communication. Here's what each letter in the DEAR MAN stands for:

D — Describe: Objectively describe the situation. Use facts, not sentiments.

E — Express: Share your thoughts and feelings about the situation. Use "I" statements.

A — Assert: Clearly state your needs or desires. Be direct and specific.

R — Reinforce: Mention the positive effects of your request for the other person and yourself.

M — Mindful: Stay focused on the issue at hand. Avoid getting sidetracked.

A — Appear confident: Use confident body language. Maintain eye contact and speak clearly.

N — Negotiate: Be willing to find a compromise if possible.

Step 3:
Roleplay and practice.

Write down a conversation based on your scenario using the DEAR MAN structure. Then, roleplay the scenario with a friend or family member.

Dialogue:

Step 4:
Reflect.

After going through the conversation, reflect on the experience:

What went well in the roleplay?

What challenges did you face?

How did using the DEAR MAN script help you express your needs effectively?

Step 5:
Apply to real life.

Apply what you've learned to a real-life situation. Engage in a conversation in which you must express your needs and desires. Remember to use the DEAR MAN script.

Real-life situation:

Step 6:
Share and discuss.

Share your real-life experience with a friend or family member. Discuss how DEAR MAN impacted the conversation:

Was it more effective for getting your point across?

What did you learn about assertive communication?

Fill this out for your specific scenario and dialogue. This worksheet is helpful for practicing and improving communication skills.

Exercise 4 — Self-Reflection on Effective Communication

Improve your communication skills through self-reflection and goal setting.

Step 1: Set the scene.
Find a comfortable and quiet space where you'll experience no interruptions.

Step 2: Choose a recent conversation.
Answer the following questions to reflect on your communication during that conversation:

 **Listening skill:** Did you actively listen during the conversation? Were you distracted or genuinely focused on the speaker's words?

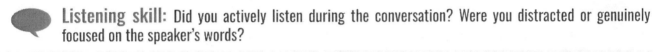 **Non-verbal communication:** How was your body language? Did it support or hinder the conversation?

💬 **Clarity and conciseness:** Were your messages clear, or did you use vague or ambiguous language?

💬 **Handling disagreements:** If there were disagreements, how did you take them? Were you respectful and open to differing viewpoints?

Step 3: Set communication goals.
Based on your reflections, set specific communication goals for yourself. For example:

I will listen actively in my next conversation and avoid interrupting.

I will use more open and empathetic body language.

I will work on expressing my thoughts more concisely.

I will practice patience and respect when conflicts arise.

Step 4: Visualize.
Close your eyes and imagine yourself successfully reaching the goals you've set for yourself regarding communication. Picture a lot of positive and productive conversations.

Step 5: Develop an action plan.
Write out the communication goals you've set for yourself and the steps needed to achieve them. For each, write out what you will do differently in your next conversation:

Step 6: Implement.
Put your goals into practice during your future interactions. After each conversation, check your progress and make necessary corrections.

Step 7: Evaluate.
At a given time you've set for yourself, evaluate your communication skills and identify where improvements are needed.

Step 8: Evaluate.
Celebrate your little wins when you achieve the goals you've set for yourself. This will keep you going.

This exercise encourages self-reflection and helps you set goals for your communication skills and achieve them. It's a fantastic way to improve your communication skills independently and watch yourself grow into a better communicator.

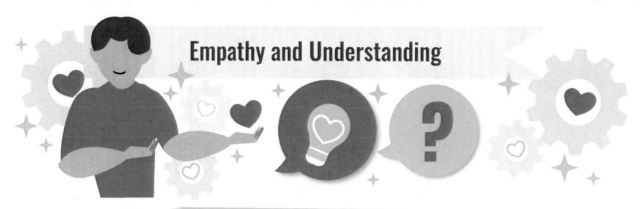

Empathy and Understanding

Have you ever heard the phrase, **"Put yourself in their shoes"** before? That's what empathy is, when you try to feel what someone else is feeling. On the other hand, understanding is about knowing and acknowledging how someone feels, even if you disagree.

When you try to be empathetic and understanding, you will notice that your relationships improve greatly, and this comes with you becoming a better friend, communicator, and problem solver. Trying to listen and understand what someone is going through makes them feel important, which goes a long way. That's the secret ingredient to cook a delicious meal of trust, strengthening the friendship.

How can you achieve this? It's not as difficult as you may think. **First, try to be a good listener.** Did you know you can hear someone without listening? It happens! Be attentive while listening, try not to interrupt the other person, ask questions about what's unclear to you, and show them you genuinely care. **Try to establish strong connections with their thoughts and emotions.**

Flip the script by picturing yourself experiencing what they're currently going through. Try to view their issues from your perspective. This isn't easy, but it will go a long way.

Roleplaying is another option you can explore. Try to act out empathy even without a real situation at hand. You and your friends can make up situations and try to be empathetic.

Even if you disagree with someone's feelings, don't invalidate them. It's okay to validate their feelings. Even when your opinion differs, respect theirs and acknowledge whatever they feel.

Also, don't limit your use of empathy and understanding to just your friends; they're tools you should use in all your relationships, whether they're family members, classmates, or romantic interests.

Proper communication with those in your life is crucial. Feel free to share your experiences, initiate questions when needed, and make your friends feel comfortable doing the same. Once you can create a safe space that's not judgmental, everyone will feel at home and won't be reluctant to open up.

By now, you should know that **empathy and understanding are two of the necessary nutrients to make your relationships stronger and more meaningful**. Try practicing them and see how much your relationships improve. You will be glad you did so.

Exercise 5 — Walk in Their Shoes

Be intentional about practicing empathy. Engage someone around you, ask about their day, and genuinely listen. Share what you learned about empathy and understanding from the conversation. Develop empathy by putting yourself in someone else's position.

Step 1: Choose an empathy target.
Think of a friend, family member, or someone in your life who is experiencing a challenging situation or significant event. Make this person your "empathy target."

Step 2: Gather information.
Try to get more details about your empathy target's experience by observing them, initiating conversations, or learning more about the situation.

Step 3: Keep a journal.
Create an Empathy Journal to document your thoughts, feelings, and discoveries as you empathize with your target.

Include:

- What you know about their situation.

- Your assumptions and judgments (if any).

- Your emotional reactions as you think of their experience.

- Any questions or uncertainties you have about their feelings or perspectives.

Step 4: Write a letter.
The receiver of this letter is your empathy target. In it, express how you see the situation and your genuine willingness to empathize and validate their feelings. Try not to offer solutions or advice.

Dear ....

Step 5: Share your empathy.

If you're comfortable doing so, share your letter with your empathy target. Let them know that you are available to listen to them without judgment.

Step 6: Reflect and adjust.

Take some time to reflect on how this exercise has affected your empathetic side. Do you notice any growth? How do you feel about showing empathy? Adjust your approach and continue to work on your empathy skills.

This exercise encourages individuals to take that bold step into another person's world and try to understand their feelings and experiences. It nurtures empathy by challenging assumptions, and it opens lines of better communication.

Conflict Resolution

Conflict resolution is the process of discussing and resolving disagreements calmly and respectfully. It's a vital skill that can help individuals, including teenagers, manage disputes judiciously. Aside from that, it will help create a good atmosphere for relationships to thrive.

You can apply conflict resolution skills to your relationships with family, friends, classmates, and coworkers. This life skill aims to find common ground, mutually understand the sides of the issue, and forge a path forward to preserve the relationship. A good grip on this skill will help you breeze through the complex nature of human interactions with confidence.

Exercise 6 Conflict Resolution

Improve your conflict resolution skills by working through a specific conflict scenario.

Scenario:

You and your friend planned to get together, but just when you're about to leave your room, they cancel your plans without a genuine reason. This hurts you, and you feel frustrated and annoyed.

Step 1: Describe the conflict.

Write down a brief description of the conflict. Add what the conflict is about, why it bothers you, and how you feel about it.

Step 2: Identify your emotions.
List the emotions you feel due to this conflict. Be specific and honest.

1

2

3

Step 3: Understand your needs.
Consider what needs or expectations were not met in this situation. Write down what you needed from your friend and how those needs were not fulfilled.

Step 4: Understand their perspective.
Now, put yourself in your friend's shoes. Think about all the possible reasons for the cancellation. Write down what might be happening in their life to make them want to cancel your plans.

Step 5: Choose a resolution approach.
Choose the approach for resolving this conflict:

- Direct communication: You will discuss the issue with your friend openly and honestly.

- Conflict mediation: You'll involve a neutral third party to help mediate the conversation.

- Let it go: You'll choose to let the issue go and not confront your friend.

Which approach will you choose and why?

Step 6: Plan the conversation.
If you choose the direct communication route, write out the points you want to discuss with your friend. Consider using "I" statements to express how you feel. Be prepared to listen to their side of the story.

Step 7: Reflect and learn.
After trying to resolve the conflict, take some time to think about the process.
Write down:

- How did the conversation go?

- What did you learn about yourself and your friend?

- What could you have done differently for a better outcome?

- What strategies can you use in the future for more effective conflict resolution?

This exercise will help you work through a real-life conflict, improve your communication skills, and increase your chances of resolving future issues with others.

Building Trust

Trust is the foundation of every healthy relationship. Be it with friends, family, or anyone else, trust is the base on which every strong relationship is built.

Trust isn't achieved suddenly; it's a gradual process. It's like a plant you nurture and care for until it reaches its maximum potential. When there's trust, the relationship is firm, sweet, and fulfilling. It's a powerful magnet that keeps connections going even when things get tough.

Exercise 7 GIVE

Enhance your interpersonal skills by practicing the **GIVE technique** in your relationships.

This technique helps you improve communication and connection in your relationships. What does GIVE stand for? Gentle, Interested, Validate, and Easy Manner. Use this exercise to practice **GIVE** in your conversations.

Gentle:
Think about a recent conversation with someone where you could have been more peaceful or kind in your communication. Write down the situation, what you said, and how you could have approached the situation more gently.

Situation	
What I said	
How could I have been gentler?	

Interested:

Consider a conversation in which you could have shown more interest in the other person's perspective or feelings. Describe the situation, your responses, and how you could have shown more interest.

Situation	
My response	
How could I have shown more interest?	

Validate:

Think of a past situation in which you could have better acknowledged the other person's feelings or viewpoint. Write out the scenario, your words or actions, and how you could have validated their perspective.

Scenario	
My words/actions	
How could I have validated their feelings?	

Easy Manner:

Think about a situation in which you were too confrontational or aggressive. Describe the situation, what you did or said, and how you could have approached the matter in an easy manner.

Situation	
My words/actions	
How could I have had an easier manner?	

Validate:

Think of a past situation in which you could have better acknowledged the other person's feelings or viewpoint. Write out the scenario, your words or actions, and how you could have validated their perspective.

Scenario	
How I will use the **GIVE** technique	

Meditate on the interaction after applying the **GIVE** technique to your chosen scenario. Think of how it felt for yourself and the other person and any changes that occurred. Write down your thoughts and any discoveries.

This exercise will strengthen your relationships by promoting better communication and understanding. Practice **GIVE** to build more positive connections with everyone around you.

Exercise 8 — Friendship Recipe

Friendships are like your best meals. You need the right ingredients to cook them up and top them with love. In this exercise, you'll create a "friendship recipe" to guide you in building and nurturing meaningful and lasting friendships. Below are the steps.

Ingredients:

List the key qualities of a great friend. Think about what you appreciate in your close friends or what you'd like to find in new ones, like loyalty, trust, humor, or kindness.

Example:
Ingredient 1: Loyalty — This means being there for your friends when they need you, standing by them in good times and bad.

Now curate your list here:

Preparation:

Describe the actions and behaviors you need to display in your friendships. Consider what role you play in making sure the bond remains strong.

Example:
Action 1: Active Listening — Make an effort to listen attentively when your friends talk. Show that you value their thoughts and feelings.

Write yours here:

Mixing Instructions:

Write down how to mix all the ingredients and actions together to form a healthy relationship. Think about how you can apply these qualities in your interactions.

Example:
Mixing Instructions — Combine active listening with kindness to create a supportive atmosphere. Add a little humor to lighten the mood and spice with trust for a strong bond. Then, stir well to taste.

Cooking Time:

How much time and effort will you put into your friendships? Consider how you can consistently maintain these connections as time passes.

Example:
Cooking Time — Dedicate regular time to my friends, like weekly or monthly calls or outings.

Taste Test:

Once your friendship "dish" is cooked, describe how you'll assess the quality of the meal. What signs let you know that a friendship is successful?

Example:
Signs of a thriving friendship — I'll know my friendship is successful when I feel valued, supported, and genuinely happy around my friends.

Serving Suggestions:

Share any extra insights for building and maintaining healthy friendships. These could be personal guidelines or self-reminders.

Example:
Serving Suggestions — Remember to celebrate your friend's successes and be there for them during tough times. Communicate openly, and don't hesitate to apologize if you make a mistake.

Share this recipe with a trusted friend or mentor if you feel comfortable doing so. Ask for feedback, and you'll be amazed at the things you learn.

Remember, building and maintaining strong and healthy friendships takes a lot of intentional effort. This recipe will help you make meaningful connections with others.

Exercise 9 FAST for Self-Respect

The **FAST** skill will help you maintain self-respect when communicating with others. **FAST** stands for **Fair**, **No Apologies**, **Stick to Values**, and **Truthful**. Let's break down each component.

Fair:
This aims for a fair and balanced conversation. Don't be too accommodating or aggressive; try to strike a balance between the two. You deserve to be respected, and you should also respect others.

No Apologies:
Do not apologize unless you need to. Over-apologizing can undermine your self-respect. Save your apologies for situations where they're needed.

Stick to Values:
Always remain true to your value system and beliefs. This does not mean you should be too rigid, but respect your principles and keep your integrity intact.

Truthful:
Be honest in your communication. Always speaking the truth is essential for self-respect.

Now, let's be practical with the **FAST** skill using an exercise:

Let's say you're working on a group assignment with classmates. One of your group members, who is known for being incompetent and unreliable, shows why he is known for that. This behavior affects your group's assignment and will affect your marks, too.

Exercise Steps:

Analyze the scenario: Think about the interaction you need to have with the unreliable group member. Consider how you can apply the FAST skill components in this situation.

FAST Components:

Note down your responses to the following questions addressing each component of the **FAST** skill:

Fair:

How can you maintain a fair approach when addressing this issue with the group member? How can you ensure you treat yourself fairly in this conversation?

No Apologies:

Are there any apologies you need to avoid in this conversation? How can you avoid over-apologizing when discussing the issue?

Stick to Values:

During this conversation, how can you stay true to your values and principles? What values do you want to uphold while addressing this challenge?

⚡ Truthful:

Consider how you can be honest and truthful when discussing the group member's behavior. In what ways can you maintain your integrity throughout the conversation?

Roleplay:

If you feel comfortable, consider roleplaying the situation with a trusted friend. Use the scenario as the context and build your conversation with your trusted friend. Then, practice applying the FAST skill during the conversation.

Reflect:

After the roleplay, take a moment to reflect on the exercise. What did you learn from applying the FAST skill in the scenario? How did it affect your sense of self-respect and confidence in the interaction?

Remember that using the **FAST** skill to practice self-respect will help you maintain your self-worth in any situation.

Chapter 8
The Journey to Personal Growth

The journey to personal growth is an adventure filled with self-discovery, learning, resilience, and celebration. By setting goals, you'll embrace learning, be resilient in overcoming challenges, build a support system, and celebrate your little wins.

This chapter will open our eyes to seeing life as a giant classroom where every life experience is a lesson waiting to be discovered. Let's say you've auditioned for the school play and failed. You don't need to feel down or bitter—think of the setback as a way to gain experience to do better next time. Every lesson counts, no matter how small.

Let's start with setting personal growth goals!

 Setting Personal Growth Goals

No doubt, life as a teenager can be overwhelming. You've experienced many changes, you're figuring out who you are, and you face new challenges daily. That can be a lot for anyone! But setting personal growth goals can be a game changer for you in this exciting yet difficult life phase.

First, let's discuss why you need personal growth. It's simple—it gives your life a direction. See goals as your road map that guide you through your teenage years. Whether you want to improve your communication skills, ace your exams, boost your confidence, or get into one of the best colleges, you need goals to keep you on the right path.

As you set goals, it's okay to aim high but ensure they are doable. With each goal completed, no matter how small, you unlock a new achievement and get an awesome feeling.

Now, it's time to make your teenage years an incredible journey of self-improvement by setting goals!

Exercise 1 My Personal Growth Goals

Your personal growth goals make you a better version of yourself. The following exercise will help you identify and plan your goals.

Instructions:

1. Write down specific areas of your life you want to improve in the "Areas of Growth" column, for example, your emotions, education, confidence, or relationships.
2. For each area of growth, set clear and specific goals. Ensure they are achievable and measurable. Write them in the "Specific Goals" column, describing what you want to achieve.
3. When do you want to achieve this goal? Write your target date for this goal in the "Timeline" column.
4. Break down each goal into smaller, more manageable steps in the "Steps to Achieve" column. This is your action plan.

Worksheet:

Areas of Growth	Specific Goals	Timeline	Steps to Achieve
1.			
2.			
3.			
4.			
5.			

Periodically check your worksheet to track your progress and mark off any goal you've completed. Since your personal growth is an ongoing journey, it's okay to be flexible and adjust as needed. Revise your goals when your priorities change and enjoy the experience.

The **SMART Goal Setting** exercise aims to help you create a structured way to achieve your goals. Using the **SMART** criteria, you can ensure your goals are Specific, Measurable, Achievable, Relevant, and Time-bound.

Ingredients:

1. Choose one of the personal growth goals you listed in the previous exercise.

2. Break down your selected goal using the following criteria:

Specific (S): What do you want to achieve?

Measurable (M): How will you measure your progress and know when you've achieved the goal?

Achievable (A): Is your goal realistic and attainable with the resources and time you have?

Relevant (R): Does your goal align with your broader objective? Is it relevant to your personal growth?

Time-Bound (T): When do you want to achieve this goal?

Use this worksheet to write your SMART goal, incorporating all the SMART criteria. Be as clear and detailed as possible.

SMART Goal	
Specific (S)	
Measurable (M)	
Achievable (A)	
Relevant (R)	
Time-Bound (T)	

3. What action steps do you need to take to achieve your goal? You can use the steps identified in the previous exercise if you use the same goal or change accordingly.

Action Steps:

1. _____

2. _____

3. _____

4. _____

5. _____

4. Regularly assess your progress and adjust if something changes.

Setting SMART goals can help you stay on the right path on your personal growth journey.

Overcoming Obstacles

You know those bumps in the road on your personal growth journey? These obstacles are just part of the adventure, and even if they make you trip, it shouldn't discourage you from pursuing your goals.

Let's discuss those obstacles and how to overcome them.

Lack of patience:
Don't see personal growth as automatic or instant; it requires patience and time. Impatience can cause a rocky road, preventing you from reaching your goal. Take your time and celebrate your small wins.

Negative self-talk:
You know that inner demon constantly discouraging you and telling you that you can't do it? It can become an obstacle, preventing you from reaching your goals. Replace negative thoughts with positive ones because you're stronger than you think.

Procrastination:
Guilty of putting things off until the last minute? When you procrastinate, your goals become overwhelming, and you might eventually abandon them halfway. Break your goals into small, manageable steps to make them easier to tackle.

Peer pressure:
Friends and classmates might not understand your goals and see them as crazy. This can get to you, forming a strong wind to push you off course. Stay on track and surround yourself with like minds to motivate and influence you positively.

These obstacles are part of your journey to success. See every challenge you encounter as a chance to learn and grow. As you continue, you'll find the path to personal growth clearer and more exciting. **You've got this, buddy!**

Exercise 3 — Obstacle-Busting Brainstorm

Your journey to success won't always be hitch-free or smooth; you'll likely face obstacles. This exercise will help you identify those potential obstacles and overcome them.

Instructions:

1. Choose the goal you want to work with. It can be one of your personal growth goals that you've set using the SMART criteria.

2. Consider the potential obstacles that you might encounter when achieving this goal. These could be internal, like fear, self-doubt, or procrastination, or external, like a lack of resources, time, or support.

Obstacle 1: _____

Obstacle 2: _____

Obstacle 3: _____

Obstacle 4: _____

Obstacle 5: _____

3. For each obstacle you've identified, write down why you see it as a challenge and its impact on your goal.

Obstacle 1 (Why is it a challenge?):

Obstacle 1 (Impact on your goal):

Obstacle 2 (Why is it a challenge?):

Obstacle 2 (Impact on your goal):

Obstacle 3 (Why is it a challenge?):

Obstacle 3 (Impact on your goal):

Obstacle 4 (Why is it a challenge?):

Obstacle 4 (Impact on your goal):

Obstacle 5 (Why is it a challenge?):

Obstacle 5 (Impact on your goal):

4. Brainstorm strategies to overcome each obstacle. These can be the resources, support, or practical steps needed.

Obstacle 1 (Strategies):

Obstacle 2 (Strategies):

Obstacle 3 (Strategies):

Obstacle 4 (Strategies):

Obstacle 5 (Strategies):

5. Based on what you've developed, create an obstacle plan outlining how to tackle each obstacle to unlock your personal growth.

Obstacle Plan:

Obstacle 1 (Plan):

Obstacle 2 (Plan):

Obstacle 3 (Plan):

Obstacle 4 (Plan):

Obstacle 5 (Plan):

By understanding and preparing ahead of your obstacles, you can stay focused and resilient as you strive for personal development.

Exercise 4 Obstacle Visualization

By visualizing potential obstacles, you can mentally prepare to overcome them. This exercise will help you gain awareness of your obstacles and visualize navigating them.

Instructions:

1. Choose a personal growth goal you've set using the SMART criteria.

2. List the obstacles that might stand in the way of achieving the goal.

Obstacle 1:

Obstacle 2:

Obstacle 3:

Obstacle 4:

Obstacle 5:

3. For each obstacle, describe how it might present itself and how it'll make you feel.

Obstacle 1 (Description):

Obstacle 2 (Description):

Obstacle 3 (Description):

Obstacle 4 (Description):

Obstacle 5 (Description):

4. Now close your eyes and imagine a scenario where you encounter one of the obstacles you've written. Visualize yourself overcoming the obstacle successfully. Imagine your actions and how you feel after conquering it.

5. Open your eyes! Write about the experience by describing how it felt to visualize overcoming obstacles, what you learned, and how the exercise will help you stay motivated and resilient.

This visualization exercise will boost your confidence and prepare you to face challenges head-on as you stay focused on your path to personal growth.

Embracing Continuous Learning

Embracing continuous learning means developing a mindset that every experience is an opportunity to learn, adapt, and grow. With a "growth mindset," your abilities and talents can be developed over time when you are dedicated and hardworking. You'll see obstacles and failures as stepping stones to success rather than roadblocks. As for mistakes, they are part of the learning process. You'll get to know areas to improve on as you refine your skills.

Reflect on your experiences by considering what you've learned from them and how they've shaped your skills and perspectives. Just as you've set goals for personal growth, set learning goals by considering the skills you want to acquire. They could be related to your hobbies, interests, or future career.

Learning will become enjoyable when it aligns with your interests or passions. As you continue, don't hesitate to seek feedback from others who are more experienced. Constructive feedback gives you a chance to understand blind spots and refine abilities.

Embracing continuous learning is an ongoing journey—you can adapt and evolve as you learn, which is entirely natural.

Exercise   5   Lifelong Learning Bucket List

Continuous learning is an exciting journey that isn't limited to formal education. It can involve skills, hobbies, or anything that interests you.

This exercise will help you create a learning list to foster a growth mindset and advance your learning.

What topics or skills are you interested in learning or exploring? Think beyond formal education. It can be hobbies, activities, or anything you've always wanted to try or understand better.

From what you've brainstormed, select your top 10 areas of interest.

1: _____

2: _____

3: _____

4: _____

5: _____

6: _____

7: _____

8: _____

9: _____

10: _____

For each area, set clear learning goals, for example, learning a new skill, reading a book, attending a seminar, or dedicating time to expand your knowledge.

Goal 1:

Goal 2:

Goal 3:

Goal 4:

Goal 5:

Goal 6:

Goal 7:

Goal 8:

Goal 9:

Goal 10:

When do you want to achieve these goals? Weeks, months, years? The timeframe adds motivation to your learning journey.

Timeframe for Goal 1:

Timeframe for Goal 2:

Timeframe for Goal 3:

Timeframe for Goal 4:

Timeframe for Goal 5:

Timeframe for Goal 6:

Timeframe for Goal 7:

Goal 8:

Goal 9:

Goal 10:

✓ Visualize yourself a few years from now—you've successfully learned and explored your 10 areas of interest. How does it feel to gain knowledge and skills in these subjects?

✓ Write your **"Lifelong Learning Bucket List"** on paper or cardboard, making it visually appealing. Visit it regularly for inspiration.

✓ Start working on your list by dedicating time and effort to achieving your learning goals. Ensure you add new ones as you check items off your list. **Remember, learning is a continuous process!**

MY GOALS

Embracing Continuous Learning Worksheet

Continuous learning keeps your mind open to new knowledge. This exercise will encourage you to reflect on your approach to learning and get the ball rolling for a lifelong commitment to personal growth.

Step 1: Identify your current attitude towards learning.
What does learning mean to you? How do you feel learning new things? What are the challenges in your learning journey?

Step 2: Know your ideal self.
What do you want to achieve? What kind of skills or knowledge do you want to acquire in the near future? What's your vision for personal growth?

Step 3: Identify areas to be explored.
What are the specific areas of interest, skills, or subjects that you want to explore?

Step 4: Set goals.
For the interests listed, set clear and achievable learning goals. They should reflect what you intend to learn or achieve within your areas of interest.

Learning Interest 1: _____

Goal: _____

Learning Interest 2: _____

Goal: _____

Learning Interest 3: _____

Goal: _____

Learning Interest 4: _____

Goal: _____

Step 5: Create an action plan.

How do you intend to pursue each learning goal? Outline your steps and consider the activities or resources needed to achieve your goals.

Learning Interest 1: _____

Learning Plan: _____

Learning Interest 2: _____

Learning Plan: _____

Learning Interest 3: _____

Learning Plan: _____

Learning Interest 4: _____

Learning Plan: _____

Step 6: Set aside time.

To achieve continuous learning, you need to allocate time for learning pursuits. When and how often can you dedicate time to your learning goals? It could be daily, weekly, or monthly.

Step 7: Seek support.

Confide in someone you trust, like a friend or family member, to encourage and hold you accountable.

Step 8: Track your progress.

You can use a personal journal to document your learning journey, achievements, obstacles, and experiences. Ensure you review your progress periodically and adjust accordingly.

Embracing continuous learning is a path to personal growth and resilience. This exercise is your guide to creating a lifelong learning plan.

Celebrating Milestones

Recognizing and celebrating small victories is like a stamp showing the milestones you've achieved and is necessary to keep yourself motivated and resilient on your growth journey. Each milestone signifies your progress, while appreciating these achievements, no matter how small they may seem, affirms that you're heading in the right direction towards a significant change or result.

As you put effort towards your personal growth goals, be intentional about appreciating your progress and results. This can be a simple, reassuring smile, giving yourself a mental pat on the back, discussing with a mentor, or journaling your accomplishments. **Recognizing your improvements reinforces your belief in your abilities and capacity for growth.**

Another way to stay motivated is by rewarding yourself when you achieve a personal growth milestone. These little rewards are powerful incentives, so don't be extravagant. Give yourself a special treat of your favorite snack, watch a movie, or take a walk in nature and take in the scenery. **Linking your personal growth achievements to a reward system reinforces the positive behaviors and habits that contribute to your growth.**

By accepting and celebrating your small victories as you grow, you motivate yourself with the right incentives and confidence to take on the next personal growth task. Remember that celebrations are powerful reminders of your milestones and proof of the progress you've made to become the best version of yourself.

Exercise 7 Milestone Map

A milestone map visually represents your life's journey, highlighting significant achievements and experiences. This exercise will help you create your personal milestone map, allowing you to deeply reflect on your life and set goals for your future.

Instructions:

1. Using paper, draw a timeline illustrating your life's events from birth to the present. You are free to express yourself creatively.

2. Mark the moment of your birth at the first point of the timeline. This is your starting point.

3. Along the timeline, highlight critical milestones, successes, and significant life events. These might include events like graduating from school, getting a job, moving to a new area, or acquiring a new skill.

4. You can use illustrations, colors, and symbols to highlight noteworthy or uplifting events that have shaped and impacted your life.

5. After reaching this point in the timeline, decide what milestones to hit. These might be career, academic, personal, or other worthwhile objectives.

6. Next to the timeline, briefly explain each of your long-term objectives. Explain the significance of these objectives to you and the steps you intend to take to fulfill them.

7. Take a moment to reflect on your milestone map. Appreciate and celebrate your personal growth, achievements, and the journey you've been on. Visualize the route you wish to take to accomplish your future goals.

8. If you feel comfortable, you can share your milestone map with your mentor, a friend, or a family member. Talk about your achievements and aspirations. There's no harm in seeking their support and encouragement.

Creating your milestone map helps you reflect on your life journey, celebrate your achievements, and set clear, inspiring future goals. Place your map where you will see and assess it daily so it can remind you of your remarkable journey and the exciting path ahead.

This worksheet can assist you in setting exciting objectives for the future, acknowledging your accomplishments, and creating a visual map of your life's path. Have fun while you draft and consider your milestone map!

Exercise 8 — Pleasant Activities List

Engaging in pleasant activities is crucial for self-care and personal growth. This worksheet is designed to help you identify, plan, and engage in enjoyable activities regularly in your life.

Instructions:

Step 1: Make your list.
List activities you find pleasant in the space below. These simple but elaborate activities should bring you joy and relaxation.

Activity 1: Reading a novel

Activity 2: _____

Activity 3: _____

Activity 4: _____

Activity 5: _____

Activity 6: _____

Step 2: Prioritize.
Next to each activity, assign a number from 1 to 5 based on how much you enjoy it, with 1 being the most enjoyable.

Activity 1: [Rating 1–5] _____

Activity 2: [Rating 1–5] _____

Activity 3: [Rating 1–5] _____

Activity 4: [Rating 1–5] _____

Activity 5: [Rating 1–5] _____

Activity 6: [Rating 1–5] _____

Step 3: Set a consistent schedule.

Consider how often you can realistically engage in these activities. Fill in the "Frequency" column with the number of times you'd like to do each activity per week or month.

Activity 1: [Frequency 1–5] _____

Activity 2: [Frequency 1–5] _____

Activity 3: [Frequency 1–5] _____

Activity 4: [Frequency 1–5] _____

Activity 5: [Frequency 1–5] _____

Activity 6: [Frequency 1–5] _____

Step 4: Plan your pleasant activities.

Make a timetable using the information you have filled in for your enjoyable activities. Think about the times and days you'll participate in each.

Activity 1: [Schedule] _____

Activity 2: [Schedule] _____

Activity 3: [Schedule] _____

Activity 4: [Schedule] _____

Activity 5: [Schedule] _____

Activity 6: [Schedule] _____

Completing this list can help you incorporate greater enjoyment and relaxation into your daily life. Making these activities a priority and scheduling them is a step toward self-care and better well-being. Participate in these enjoyable activities regularly to improve your personal growth and resilience.

Building a Support System

As you continue your personal growth journey, never forget that you are not alone; therefore, you don't have to journey alone. **Building a robust network or support system is like having a group of cheerleaders encouraging you from the sidelines.** This group of people cheering on you are your source of inspiration and safety net. So, let's dive into what a support system entails and how to build one that can empower you on your path to personal growth.

Your support network includes mentors, friends, family, and support groups—they help you through life's highs and lows. These individuals provide support, guidance, and a listening ear. **They are essential because they offer a variety of viewpoints and an outsider's point of view, which aids in decision-making and problem-solving.**

Your support system is a network of relationships built on mutual respect, trust, and shared ideals. It is not only about asking for assistance when you need it. This support network may grow into a strong force that helps you advance in your quest for personal development by enabling you to overcome setbacks, recognize successes, and become the finest version of yourself.

Exercise 9 — Support Network

Building a solid support network is essential to your personal growth and development. Using this worksheet, you may develop a strategy to fortify your support system, build resilience, and locate possible sources of assistance.

Step 1: Identify sources of support.
Find and list people, groups, or organizations that can be part of your network and support system. Include family members, friends, teachers, mentors, support groups, or any other source of support.

Friend: [Name]

Family Member: [Name]

Teacher: [Name]

Mentor: [Name]

Support Group: [Name]

Step 2: Define their roles.
Describe how each support source can contribute to your personal growth and resilience. Also, describe the kind of support you can expect from them.

Friend: [Provide emotional support and listen well.]

Family Member:

Teacher:

Mentor:

Support Group:

Step 3: Reach out.

Strategize and plan how to contact each possible source of help, for example, by chatting, sending a message, or setting up frequent get-togethers.

Friend: [Call or text to check in and arrange get-togethers.]

Family Member:

Teacher:

Mentor:

Support Group:

Step 4: Commit and communicate.

Commit to staying in touch with your sources of assistance regularly. Note that effective communication is key to maintaining a strong support system.

Friend: [I will call every week to chat.]

Family Member:

Teacher:

Mentor:

Support Group:

Step 5: Evaluate and adjust.

Regularly evaluate the effectiveness of your support system. Ask yourself if your needs are being met. Make changes and adjustments to your support network to fit your needs if necessary.

Periodically revisit and update your support system to ensure it remains a valuable part of your personal growth journey. Feel free to add or adjust steps and sources according to your needs and circumstances.

Having a solid support network may provide you with the inspiration, direction, and emotional support you need to overcome and navigate challenges in life and carry on with your path to resilience and personal growth.

Exercise 10 Gratitude Circle

Building a support system is not based on finding people but on appreciating those who already support you. The next exercise will help you recognize and acknowledge the people who contribute to your well-being.

♥ ## Step 1: Identify your circle.
Draw a large circle on your writing material and write your name in the center.

♥ ## Step 2: Identify the inner circle.
Consider the individuals closest to you, especially those who consistently show you love and support. These are the people you can always rely on.

Draw a circle close to your name and call this circle the "Inner Support System." In this new circle, write the names or initials of the people you've identified.

♥ ## Step 3: Identify close friends and family.
Now, think of your friends and family who provide you with encouragement and support. These are the individuals who are important to you. Put their initials or names in the center circle surrounding the innermost one. Name this group "Close Friends and Family."

♥ ## Step 4: Identify your outer circle.
Finally, consider other people, such as teachers, mentors, colleagues, or acquaintances, who support you and contribute to your personal growth and resilience. Put their names or initials in the outermost circle around the others. Name this circle "Extended Support Network."

♥ ## Step 5: Reflect and express gratitude.
Take a moment to reflect on those you have assigned to each circle. Think about the ways that they assist you. What actions have they taken that have improved your life?

For each person, write a short note or message expressing your appreciation and thanks for their help. Although you are not required to send these messages, writing them can be a meaningful exercise.

This exercise helps you visualize your support network. You will better identify and value the people who help you develop your resilience and personal growth. By recognizing their positive influence, you strengthen your relationships and cultivate gratitude.

Conclusion

CBT

Well done, buddy!

It's been a wonderful ride with you, and I am glad you hung in there.

So far, we've discussed how you can use the skills and techniques of CBT and DBT to control your emotions, build resilience, silence negative self-talk, manage stress, cultivate self-compassion, and nurture healthy relationships.

I believe you've now unlocked your emotional superpowers!

Whether you're a teen struggling with your emotions or a parent seeking to understand and guide your child, this book is your toolkit for a life worth living.

As you conclude this book, remember that if I, who was once overwhelmed by anxiety and battled self-doubt for many years, can embrace my inner strengths and live without emotional baggage, you can too.

Use this book however it clicks with you. Embrace the exercises and techniques that resonate most and commit to them. After all, it's your path to liberation and living a happier and more fulfilling life.

Finally, we'd love to hear about your thoughts, journey, and progress. Leave a review and let others know how this book has impacted you. Remember, everyone deserves a life worth living. **Share the good news and help others discover their emotional superpowers!**

Don't stop now— your extraordinary life is just beginning!

Reference List

American Psychological Association. (n.d.). Cognitive-Behavioral Therapy. https://www.apa.org/ptsd-guideline/patients-and-families/cognitive-behavioral

Anxiety and Depression Association of America (ADAA). (n.d.). Tips to Manage Anxiety and Stress. https://adaa.org/tips-manage-anxiety-and-stress

Beck Institute for Cognitive Behavior Therapy. (2023, January.). The Power of a Pledge: Putting CBT in Action https://beckinstitute.org/blog/the-power-of-a-pledge-putting-cbt-in-action/

DBT Self Help. (n.d.). What Is DBT? https://dbtselfhelp.com/what-is-dbt/

DBT Self Help. (n.d.). Emotion Regulation Skills. https://dbtselfhelp.com/dbt-skills-list/emotion-regulation/

DBT Self Help. (n.d.). Interpersonal Effectiveness Skills. https://dbtselfhelp.com/dbt-skills-list/interpersonal-effectiveness/

DBT Self Help. (n.d.). Distress Tolerance Skills. https://dbtselfhelp.com/dbt-skills-list/distress-tolerance/

DBT Self Help. (n.d.). Mindfulness Skills. https://dbtselfhelp.com/dbt-skills-list/mindfulness/

Good Therapy. (n.d.). What Is Dialectical Behavior Therapy (DBT)? https://www.goodtherapy.org/learn-about-therapy/types/dialectical-behavioral-therapy

Greater Good Magazine: Science-Based Insights for a Meaningful Life. (n.d.). Practice Kindness? Start with Yourself. https://greatergood.berkeley.edu/article/research_digest/practice_kindness_start_with_yourself

Harvard Health Publishing. (2014, January). Simple Steps to a Healthier, Happier You. https://www.health.harvard.edu/staying-healthy/simple-steps-to-get-happier-and-healthier

HealthyPlace. (2021, July). Trauma Stands Between Us and Healthy Communication https://www.healthyplace.com/blogs/relationshipsandmentalillness/2021/7/trauma-stands-between-us-and-healthy-communication

Mayo Clinic. (n.d.). Cognitive Behavioral Therapy. https://www.mayoclinic.org/tests-procedures/cognitive-behavioral-therapy/about/pac-20384610

Mind. (n.d.). Cognitive Behavioural Therapy (CBT). https://www.mind.org.uk/information-support/drugs-and-treatments/cognitive-behavioural-therapy-cbt/#.YgJZ-_IKiUk

Mindful. (2019, August). A 10-Minute Guided Meditation to Foster Forgiveness. https://www.mindful.org/10-minute-guided-mindfulness-meditation-foster-forgiveness/

Mindful. (2015, August). Four Steps to Freedom from Negative Thinking. https://www.mindful.org/four-steps-to-freedom-from-negative-thinking/

Mindful Schools. (n.d.). A Mindful Approach to Growth Mindset and Performing Under Pressure. https://www.mindfulschools.org/inspiration/mindful-growth-mindset-and-performing-under-pressure/

National Institute of Mental Health. (n.d.). Generalized Anxiety Disorder: When Worry Gets Out of Control. https://www.nimh.nih.gov/health/topics/generalized-anxiety-disorder-gad/index.shtml

PositivePsychology.com. (2019, April). What is Goal Setting and How to Do it Well. https://positivepsychology.com/goal-setting/

Psych Central. (June, 2021). All About Cognitive Behavioral Therapy (CBT). https://psychcentral.com/lib/in-depth-cognitive-behavioral-therapy

Psychology Today. (2023, January). 5 Tips to Help You Set Better Goals. https://www.psychologytoday.com/intl/blog/social-instincts/202301/5-tips-to-help-you-set-better-goals

Psychology Today. (2019, February). 5 Tips for Setting Healthy Goals. https://www.psychologytoday.com/us/blog/supersurvivors/201902/5-tips-setting-healthy-goals

Psychology Today. (2022, August). 8 Elements of a Healthy Relationship. https://www.psychologytoday.com/intl/blog/invisible-bruises/202208/8-elements-healthy-relationship

Psychology Today. (2018, December). What Does a Healthy Relationship Look Like? https://www.psychologytoday.com/us/blog/friendship-20/201812/what-does-healthy-relationship-look

Psychology Today. (n.d.). Cognitive Behavioral Therapy. https://www.psychologytoday.com/us/basics/cognitive-behavioral-therapy

Psychology Today. (2023, September). 8 Simple Strategies to Boost Self-Compassion. https://www.psychologytoday.com/intl/blog/conquering-codependency/202306/8-simple-strategies-to-boost-self-compassion

Psychology Today. (2017, March). How to Cultivate More Self-Compassion.   https://www.psychologytoday.com/intl/blog/nurturing-self-compassion/201703/how-cultivate-more-self-compassion

Psychology Today. (2012, September). How to Stop Negative Thoughts From Ruining Your Day. https://www.psychologytoday.com/intl/blog/trust-yourself/202302/how-to-prevent-negative-thoughts-from-ruining-your-day

Psychology Today. (2015, September). 7 Ways to Deal With Negative Thoughts. https://www.psychologytoday.com/us/blog/women-s-mental-health-matters/201509/7-ways-deal-negative-thoughts

Psycom. (2023, January). What is Cognitive Behavioral Therapy (CBT)? Exploring the Concept and Its Benefits. https://www.psycom.net/what-is-cognitive-behavioral-therapy-cbt

Think CBT. (n.d.). Think CBT Worksheets. https://thinkcbt.com/think-cbt-worksheets

University of Washington, School of Social Work. (n.d.). A Therapist's Guide To Brief Cognitive Behavioral Therapy. https://depts.washington.edu/dbpeds/therapists_guide_to_brief_cbtmanual.pdf

Verywell Mind. (2023, February). How to Stop Negative Thoughts. https://www.verywellmind.com/how-to-change-negative-thinking-3024843

Verywell Mind. (2023, May). Dialectical Behavior Therapy (DBT): Definition, Techniques, and Benefits. https://www.verywellmind.com/dialectical-behavior-therapy-1067402

WebMD. (2021, September). Stop Negative Thinking. https://www.webmd.com/balance/features/accentuating-a-positive-attitude#:~:text=Be%20gentle%20with%20yourself.,isn't%20helpful%20to%20you.

WebMD. (2022, February). Therapeutic Ways to Change Negative Thoughts. https://www.webmd.com/depression/features/therapy-change-negative-thoughts

Worry Wise Kids. (n.d.). Cognitive Behavior Therapy and Medications. Retrieved from https://worrywisekids.org/node/22

Made in United States
North Haven, CT
15 December 2023

45820280R00100